The
Billion Dollar
Hangover

OTHER BOOKS BY CARL A. COPPOLINO, M.D.

PRACTICE OF HYPNOSIS IN ANESTHESIOLOGY
FREEDOM FROM FAT

The Billion Dollar Hangover

CARL A. COPPOLINO, M.D.
CARMELA M. COPPOLINO, M.D.

New York: A. S. Barnes and Company, Inc.
London: Thomas Yoseloff Ltd

Library of Congress Catalogue Card Number: 65-18583

A. S. Barnes and Co., Inc.
8 East 36th Street
New York, New York 10016

Thomas Yoseloff Ltd
18 Charing Cross Road
London W.C.2, England

6313
Printed in the United States of America

1346169

For Our Parents

Preface*

Alcoholism is an illness. Ugly and unhappy but, with patience and honesty, a treatable illness.

From the point of view of the employer, the alcoholic is an employee at any level in the organization whose work is unsatisfactory because of his compulsive, excessive, repetitive drinking. He thereby becomes the legitimate concern of his employer.

Although generally small in number in any given company, they pose an exceedingly difficult and perplexing personnel problem. They are also costly in terms of absenteeism, accidents, sick payments, turnover, lost production, lowered morale, faulty judgment, bad decisions, and damaging public and customer relationships.

With respect to an employee suffering from alcoholism, the combination of unsatisfactory performance, excessive costs, and the almost certain progressive deterioration of the individual if the illness goes unchecked, creates a situation which conscientious management and supervision should neither tolerate nor ignore.

Alcoholism is progressive, deteriorating, and devastating. It destroys the drinker and his family. It puts great burdens on his

* Kemper Insurance Company, Chicago, Illinois.

friends. It is estimated that the 3,000,000 employed problem drinkers cost their companies two billion dollars. That's quite a hangover.

Carl A. Coppolino, M.D.

Carmela M. Coppolino, M.D.

Acknowledgments

We have received valuable information and assistance from the following groups:

1. Committee on Alcoholism of the American Medical Association;
2. Yale Center of Alcohol Studies at Rutgers University, New Jersey;
3. National Council on Alcoholism Inc., New York, New York;
4. Kemper Insurance, Chicago, Illinois.

We wish to make special mention of the following organizations which made major contributions to the indicated portions of the manuscript:

1. Hoffman-La Roche Incorporated, Nutley, New Jersey (Part I);
2. The Christopher D. Smithers Foundation of New York (Part II).

Contents

Introduction *

By Sidney Greenberg

It has been said that the alcoholic is everybody's business; he should be particularly a problem of business. In the last ten years, industry has been increasingly aware of the need to deal constructively with employees who have drinking problems. As Dr. J. L. Norris of the Eastman Kodak Company has said, "A company that says it does not have any problem with alcoholism among its employees does not know what it is talking about."

Even on the basis of the most conservative estimates, there are today at least 700,000 problem drinkers employed in non-agricultural industries, and at least 100,000 alcoholics in agricultural industries. This is based on a very conservative estimate of an incidence of 1.2 per 100 population, as obtained from recent census figures.

There is a work force in the U.S. of more than 70,000,000. Of the two and a half to three million who have a problem with drinking, only about one in 20 can be considered a problem drinker. An alcoholic employee loses three weeks annually because of alcoholism and two days more than other employees

* From "Industry, Its Problems with Alcoholism," A Symposium on the Treatment and Rehabilitation of the Alcoholic, Sept. 26, 1962.

due to other illnesses. His accident rate is usually twice that of his co-workers and his life span is reduced by an average of 12 years. The time lost by alcoholic employees amounts to an approximate total of 40,000,000 work days a year. We must also remember that a great number of these are working only part-days on their poorly productive hangover days.

The immense direct loss to industry can be partially measured by the amount of time lost in absenteeism; the cost of replacement of skilled and unskilled workers, who are usually fired at the peak of their productive lives; and by the cost of hospitalization and disability pay to these known alcoholics. As well, we find many hidden losses, such as accidents, increased inefficiency and waste, slow-downs, lowering of morale among the other workers and staff, and increased costs of pension and disability programs. It is also estimated that for each individual having an alcohol problem, four other individuals are directly and indirectly involved.

The number of alcoholics in any given industry varies with the locale of the plant, the ratio of men to women employed, and also with the age and geographic origin of the employees. Thus a plant located in a small town where drinking is frowned upon, and which employs mostly young women of southern European, Asian, or Hebrew descent, will have a relatively small problem.

Increasing education in the field of alcoholism, perhaps stimulated by the Yale School of Alcoholic Studies and other such centers, has resulted in industrial awareness of this problem. But the main factors were financial. These caused the attitude of industrial management toward employees with an alcohol problem to change within the last few years. This change began during and after the last war, when it became difficult to obtain experienced replacements for discharged alcoholic employees. Many of them recognize that alcoholic rehabilitation is possible.

Previously, industry simply handled the problem by punishing the employee with dismissal. All this has been gradually altered in the last ten years. A successful program to deal with the problems of excessive drinking which occur in industry can only come from the cooperation of labor, management, the industrial medical department, government compensation programs, the medical profession, and the research teams.

To be able to treat these individuals, one must be able to find them, preferably early, and this is not always that easy. We all know that the results of excessive drinking are often masked by being attributed to other causes. Excessive absenteeism and frequent lateness, increased accident rates, decreased production due to inefficiency, errors in judgment and bad public relations are not entered on employees' records as being due to alcohol. His fellow employees, even his foreman and the higher executives, consciously and unconsciously hide the problem or avoid facing it if they don't know what to do about it.

Early detection is most difficult. There is no definite agreement as to what constitutes the pre-alcoholic. However, we could detect some cases earlier if friends and relatives did not protect the one with the problem. The alcoholic is using alcohol for himself as a "cover-up"; in addition, his well-meaning friends, fellow-employees, and relatives cover for him. The early alcoholic can "get by" sometimes because of the social acceptance of alcohol by some groups. But when his associates notice a problem, they often take a protective attitude—they "give the guy a break," they "don't squeal," they "don't get him in Dutch"—and knowledge of his problem does not reach management for some time. Reports of absences, tardiness, and inefficiency are pushed aside. This is accomplished with the help of friends, sometimes his own family physician, and sometimes even the plant physician. The family feels ashamed or has feelings of guilt, and then pleads for this type of meaningless help.

The early alcoholic then deteriorates into an uncontrollable case. He will do anything to avoid detection and will continually deny the truth in spite of the presented facts. He has poor insight and strong defenses. He does not want to give up what he has, false protection against his problems. We must remember that even the early alcoholic begins to go through these stages:

1. He says, "I can take it or leave it alone." But he can't.
2. He develops alibis, such as "I'm expected to drink in my type of job or business."
3. He takes a drink for that hangover feeling the morning after in order to be able to get to the job.
4. He shifts to less potent liquids, such as beer or wine, but not for long.
5. He begins the alcoholic decline with the development of anti-social behavior and by drinking alone.
6. He loses his friends and stays away from his job and loved ones.

Therefore, emphasis should be upon prevention and upon treatment at an early stage—before drinking becomes a serious medical problem. This can also be more readily and efficiently instituted in an industrial setting. The handling of this problem is not a task for the industrial physician or psychiatrist individually, but for a working team.

Industry is beginning to recognize this group of employees as sick people, and should attempt to help them within the industrial medical setting, especially if they are valuable, well-trained, and devoted employees. Many industrial organizations, particularly large ones, have psychiatric divisions in their medical departments. Early recognition of the problem drinker establishes a better possibility for rehabilitation, which is a more intelligent approach than disciplinary action.

Labor has adopted an intelligent attitude toward this problem and frequently "sits in" with the medical department and management in deciding cases. They now know that other employees, the foreman, supervisors, and the union steward must be educated about this problem and be made to realize the mistake of covering up for the alcoholic. They then look to management for a clearly defined program to follow in the handling of a fellow employee with a drinking problem. Referrals to the family doctor, the priest, rabbi or minister, or to AA all have their place, but in industry we feel that the combined clinical team approach has the most to offer the patient. Labor wants this type of program. They do not want one that is based on disciplinary measures alone. Some ask that after discussion between the offending employee and his foreman and steward, and after the failure of some preliminary warnings, the employee should justifiably be put on probation and referred for medical evaluation. They also realize that this treatment program may be a long-term one.

An early detection plan has been set up in some industries and more advanced programs have been instituted by others. Several companies have already established full rehabilitation programs, although in many there is considerable variation in the nature and the extent of the treatment that is offered. One of the earliest was that started by the Allis-Chalmers Company of Milwaukee, with only an instruction program for their supervisory staff, plus a counsellor. This counsellor took on problems of loans, social rehabilitation at home, housing problems, etc., as they applied to alcoholics. But his main job was to stress, in his lectures to supervisors, not to try to help the problem drinker with amateur advice, or to take their own disciplinary action against him. They were told, "Refer him to a source of help and you will salvage an experienced, able worker who otherwise might be lost." With that alone, the absenteeism rate fell in four years from 8 per cent to 3 per cent in a known group of problem drinkers. They then worked closely with AA people and particularly with the industrial physician and a psychiatrist. Some other companies concerned themselves only with the diagnosis and the classification of problem drinkers. They therefore resorted to therapy only outside of the company and this was planned according to each individual case. If the case needed hospitalization, psychiatric treatment, or referral to membership in AA, the patient was treated and directed along those paths. The Standard Oil Company of New Jersey was one of the earliest to have such a program. However, in 1952 they began to see that this was not a complete plan, and joined in the use and support of the Consultation Clinic at New York University. The medical director of another company, DuPont, reported that the most successful method of handling the alcoholic in his company is with the cooperation and help of AA, a member of which is associated with their medical staff. The Eastman Kodak Company also makes extensive utilization of AA and has supplemented this program with a community program which the company has helped to develop.

The Consolidated Edison Company of New York developed still another approach. In late 1947, the company began to recognize alcoholism as a medical condition and adopted a company procedure for this problem. The procedure was aimed primarily at early recognition of the employee with a drinking problem, rehabilitation of the employee where possible, and, when not possible, the establishment of a justifiable basis for disability retirement. The company first interviewed the employee, discussed the problem with his supervisor, put the employee on probation, and referred him to their own medical department for therapy. They even tried to handle domestic situations if these presented difficulties. This program, although minimal, was much more than anything ever offered before. Finally, in 1951, Dr. John Witmore, the former medical di-

rector of the company, proposed a plan of treatment and rehabilitation to be carried out in a special center *outside* the company setting. As a result of his planning and consultation
with New York University, in January, 1952, the Consolidated Edison Company volunteered to underwrite the cost
for the establishment of a Consultation Center for Alcoholism, which was established at the University Hospital of the
New York University Bellevue Medical Center. This clinic, the
first to be devoted solely to the alcoholic in industry, was opened
in February of 1952.

Industry's stake in this problem is partly financial. A well
instituted program results in increased efficiency and morale,
and a large financial saving for the worker and the company.
Industry should deal not only with the individual's acute alcohol problem or with classification of the alcoholic, but with
the problems of prevention. By establishment of information
bureaus, and by counseling and helping employees and their
families who have special emotional problems, companies will
help to make their employees less vulnerable to alcoholism.
The burden of failure does not fall in the man on the alcoholic employee, but on the industrial community in which he
works, which must continually devise new means of reaching
him. Alcoholism is a social tragedy; in addition, no company
can stand to afford the economic waste. The employee is usually valuable and frequently has great future potential. But
when his alcoholic problem is not recognized, or when the
company does not face up to the problem, inefficiency and
deterioration—and eventually the complete loss of a trained
employee—result, which the company can ill afford. Many studies show the end results of rehabilitation to be poor; others,
like ours, give reason for great hope.

Even if the dividends earned by these programs seem to be
small, they are still dividends. One must often evaluate each

case separately. A program that succeeds in rehabilitating a key employee may pay more dividends than one which helps two or three rank-and-file employees or which fails with ten advanced cases. In many cases treatment comes too late; sometimes it is too costly. We are then left with the greater problem of prevention. Education of all employees, early pre-employment screening, possibly by psychometric testing and/or by having complete social and environmental studies of each employee, or even by having a central register of employees in each industry, have all been suggested as possible steps in prevention.

Supervisory personnel should also be educated separately to improve their techniques of detection. Medical departments must of necessity play the major role in this program, in spite of the fact that the causes and treatment are not certainly defined and not wholly medical in nature. Labor and management are taking good strong steps on the road to developing and improving rehabilitation techniques for the alcoholic. Some of the plans appear to be practical and effective. Perhaps with more organized research and/or with organized government programs, this great medical problem could be more effectively dealt with, as are other chronic and destructive diseases. Perhaps in the future there will be methods to handle the other psychosomatic problems encountered in industry.

Industry must accept the challenge of alcoholism and set examples for further programs to help control and relieve this physical and social suffering and concurrent economic loss.

Part I
General Aspects
of Alcoholism

1 An 18th-Century Physician's View of Alcoholism

The belief that so potent a liquid as alcohol must be capable of causing serious disease is an old one. Benjamin Rush[1] in his famous *Inquiry into the Effects of Ardent Spirits Upon the Human Body and Mind,* assured his readers that "ardent spirits" dispose the body "to every form of acute disease; they moreover excite fevers in persons predisposed to them, from other causes." Among the diseases which "are the usual consequences of the habitual use of ardent spirits," Rush listed:

1. A decay of appetite, sickness at stomach, and a puking of bile or a discharge of a frothy and viscid phlegm by hawking, in the morning;

2. Obstructions of the liver . . .

3. Jaundice and dropsy of the belly and limbs and finally of every cavity in the body . . .

4. Hoarseness, and a husky cough, which often terminate in consumption and sometimes in an acute and fatal disease of the lungs;

5. Diabetes, that is, a frequent and weakening discharge of pale, or sweetish urine;

6. Redness, and eruptions on different parts of the body. They generally begin in the nose, after gradually extending all over the

face, sometimes extend to the limbs in the form of leprosy. They have been called "Rumbuds" when they appear in the face . . .

7. A fetid breath, composed of every thing that is offensive in putrid animal matter;

8. Frequent and disgusting belchings . . .

9. Epilepsy;

10. Gout, in all its various forms of swelled limbs, colic, palsy and apoplexy; lastly,

11. Madness . . .

Today, some two centuries later, many laymen would probably still consider this a reasonably accurate, although overwrought, picture of alcohol's destructive powers; and they could point to a sufficient number of individuals "shattered" in mind or body to back up their arguments.

Twentieth-century research, however, while it hardly establishes alcohol as a benign and milk-like beverage, does tend to soften its image somewhat. Alcohol is indeed implicated in a number of varied diseases, but its role in most cases appears to be an *indirect* one. "The net effect of a brief survey of some of the fairly numerous conditions popularly and clinically associated with alcoholism," according to E. E. Lape,[2] "is to deprive alcohol of a direct causal role and to focus attention on the general malnutrition, specific nutritional deficiencies, the metabolic derangements in psychoses, neuropathies, pellagra, liver cirrhosis and other pathological conditions frequently found in alcoholics—but not peculiar to them."

SOME OF ALCOHOL'S MORE DIRECT EFFECTS

Alcohol's chief pharmacologic action is on the central nervous system where it acts as a depressant, slowing down and hampering both motor performance, such as the control of speech and eye movements, and mental function.

(a) Alcoholic intoxication: "singing, hallooing, roaring." Drunkenness is easily the most common clinical manifestation of alcoholism and its psychological and physical effects have been recorded by countless observers. One of the most graphic descriptions of the intoxicated individual was sketched by Rush. Among the symptoms which characterize the drunkard, he noted:

. . . certain extravagant acts which indicate a temporary fit of madness. These are singing, halooing, roaring, imitating the noises of brute animals, jumping, tearing off clothes, dancing naked, breaking glasses and china, and dashing other articles of household furniture upon the ground or floor.

After a while the paroxysm of drunkenness is completely formed. The face now becomes flushed, the eyes project, and are somewhat watery, winking is less frequent than is natural; the under lip is protruded . . . the head inclines a little to one shoulder; . . . the jaw falls; . . . belchings and hickup [*sic*] take place; . . . the limbs totter; . . . the whole body staggers; . . . the unfortunate subject of this history next falls on his seat; . . . he looks around him with a vacant countenance, and mutters inarticulate sounds to himself; . . . he attempts to rise and walk. In this attempt, he falls upon his side, from which he gradually turns upon back.

He now closes his eyes, and falls into a profound sleep, frequently attended by snoring, and profuse sweats, and sometimes with such a relaxation of the muscles which confine the bladder and the lower bowels, as to produce a symptom which delicacy forbids me to mention. In this condition, he often lies from ten, twelve, and twenty-four hours, to two, three, and four and five days, an object of pity and disgust to his family and friends.

Since the signs of intoxication are quite distinctive, to say the least, they generally present no problem in diagnosis. Coma, of course, is the one exception; diagnosis of alcoholic coma can never be safely made merely on the basis of a flushed face, stupor, and the odor of alcohol, but only after the careful exclusion of other causes. Almost all the signs of intoxication result from alcohol's depressant action on nerve cells in certain selected parts of the nervous system, possibly the upper brainstem and diencephalon, in a manner similar to that of the barbiturates or inhalant anesthesia. Unlike the general anesthetics, however, the safety margin is a narrow one, and the ingestion of too much alcohol can cause the irreversible depression of respiration which accounts for the occasional coma fatality.[3]

(b) Abstinence withdrawal syndrome: "tremulous, hallucinatory, convulsive, delirious." When the alcoholic has stopped drinking for a while, he is subject to a second constellation of symptoms. These, too, the sharp-eyed Dr. Rush has set down:

His recovery from this fit of intoxication is marked with several peculiar appearances. He opens his eyes, and closes them again; . . . he gapes and stretches his limbs . . . he then coughs and pukes; . . . his voice is hoarse, . . . he rises with difficulty, and staggers to a chair; his eyes resemble balls of fire, . . . his hands tremble, . . . he loathes the sight of food; . . . he calls for a glass of spirits to compose his stomach . . . now and then he emits a deep-fetched sigh, or groan, from a transient twinge of conscience, but he more frequently scolds, and curses every thing around him. In this state of languor and stupidity, he remains for two or three days, before he is able to resume his former habits of business and conversation.

This time, Dr. Rush actually understated his case. The alcoholic seen most often by physicians—particularly by hospital staffs—is often in an even worse condition. Morrison,[4] describing a group of 168 alcoholics hospitalized in his alcoholism clinic, noted that many were acutely ill on admission.

They were nervous, tremulous, weak, and many had abdominal pains with nausea and vomiting. Most were dehydrated as shown by increased blood hematocrit indicative of hemoconcentration. Practically all complained of insomnia. On physical examination, most patients had gross tremors of the extremities, injected eyes, and flushed faces. Disorders other than alcoholism including diabetes mellitus, psychosis, fracture, cirrhosis, gouty arthritis, and others were encountered in 12 patients.

According to Victor and Adams, "the shakes"—a state of tremulousness often combined with general irritability, nausea, and vomiting—is the most frequent cause for admission of an alcoholic to the hospital. Delirium tremens is apparently a severer form of the same condition with even more intense psychomotor and speech overactivity, autonomic over-activity (sweating, tachycardia, dilated pupils, and fever), more profound disorders of perception (resulting in auditory and visual hallucinations), and greater confusion. Distinctly a serious illness, it has a mortality rate of 15% in these investigators' experience. Death frequently occurs because of the complications of trauma and infections or, more directly, because of peripheral circulatory collapse or hyperthermia.

At first glance, both the acute alcoholic episode and the withdrawal phase would seem to result from the toxic effects of alcohol. The symptoms of toxicity however—slurred speech, staggering, stupor—are quite different from the symptom complex of tremor, hallucinosis, and delirium. The first state is associated with a high level of alcohol in the blood, the second with a low or negligible level. Perhaps most significant, continued use of alcohol not only intensifies the symptoms of intoxication but can actually nullify symptoms such as nausea, vomiting, and tremor. Based on their own studies and those of Isbell,[5] Victor and Adams postulate that, in the chronic alcoholic, the neurologic symptoms of withdrawal "are the result of excessive and disorganized activity of those parts of the central nervous system normally acted upon by alcohol, after the diminution in the levels of blood alcohol, viz., after sleep or enforced abstinence."

MANAGEMENT OF THE WITHDRAWAL PHASE

Just as the signs of intoxication and withdrawal usually present little problem in differential diagnosis, the management of these conditions also follows well-known patterns. They are, however, a far cry from the patterns recognized in Rush's day. Among other "remedies" for a fit of drunkenness, Rush suggested thrusting a feather down the patient's throat to induce vomiting, plunging him into cold water, terrifying him into sobriety, provoking "profuse sweats" in him or even severely whipping him in order to excite "a revulsion of the blood from the brain, to the external parts of the body."

The distressing withdrawal symptoms demand expert medical attention, often in a hospital setting. Typical treatment given to patients in an alcoholic clinic was outlined by Morrison in a recently published study. At the time of admission, all patients routinely received one of the newer psychopharmaceuticals either intramuscularly or orally. Adjusted doses of the agent were administered throughout the patient's stay. In addition, all received "two daily intravenous injections of 1,000 cc. of 10 per cent fructose in water plus liberal quantities of fruit juices to correct dehydration, 12 units of regular insulin to hasten the metabolism of alcohol, and 2 cc. of vitamin B complex intramuscularly to combat avitaminosis." In three cases, ACTH was administered concurrently for the control of alcoholic hallucinosis.

On this regimen, response was good in all but five of 168 patients. The psychopharmaceutical's value was stressed since it "gave marked relief of anxiety, tension and tremor in many patients, and . . . relieved one of the most distressing of all symptoms for these patients—inability to sleep." The agent used in this study, Librium (chlordiazepoxide HC1), was found particularly useful because it not only prevented withdrawal convulsions in all patients but, by providing a favorable mental outlook, "also seemed to counteract the morbid anesthetic depression so often produced by the continued use of alcohol."

NOTES

1. B. Rush, *Inquiry into the Effects of Ardent Spirits Upon the Human Body and Mind* (Brookfield: E. Merriam & Co., ed. 8, 1814). Reprinted in *Quart. J. Stud. Alcohol*, 4:321, 1943.
2. E. E. Lape (ed.), *Medical Research: A Midcentury Survey* (Boston: Little, Brown & Co., 1955), vol. 2, p. 537.
3. M. Victor and R. D. Adams, *Am. J. Clin. Nutrition*, 9:379, 1961.
4. J. M. Morrison, *Dis. Nerv. System*, 24:430, 1963.
5. H. Isbell, *et. al.*, *Quart. J. Stud. Alcohol*, 16:1, 1955.

2 Alcoholism

What is alcoholism? Definitions of it are many; for the practicing physician as well as for the layman, the following may be the most helpful.

//Alcoholism is a chronic illness, psychic or somatic or psychosomatic, which manifests itself as a disorder of behavior. It is characterized by the repeated drinking of alcoholic beverages to an extent that exceeds customary dietary use or compliance with the social customs of the community, and that interferes with the drinker's health or his social or economic functioning.// Many special categories of alcoholics have been identified, including "alcohol addicts," who cannot control their drinking, and "alcoholics with complications." The latter are those whose excessive drinking has led to recognizable physical or mental complications.[1]

This definition, its authors point out, encompasses the entire range of persons whose patterns of excessive drinking, presumably dictated by underlying problems, result in identifiable untoward effects. It defines a condition which belongs in the realm of public health, but excludes the occasional excessive drinker whose disorderly conduct or automobile accident makes him more the concern of the civil authorities than of health personnel.

PREVALENCE

There are 5,000,000 alcoholics in the United States, it is estimated,[2] of whom 1,250,000 are suffering the complications of alcoholism. These figures give the U.S. a rate of 4,760 cases per 100,000 adults. The ratio of males to females is 5.8 to 1. The rate of alcoholism varies from state to state (see Table 1). California ranks highest according to the latest available statistics, followed by New Jersey, New Hampshire, and New York.

As might be expected, urban areas have a higher rate of alcoholism than rural areas. The size of the city is not the decisive factor, however (see Table 2). For example, New York City, although its rate of alcoholism is high, is outranked by several smaller cities.

Contrary to popular opinion, only about 7 per cent of the total number of alcoholics can be found on the skid rows of America.[3] The great majority of alcoholics (at least 85 per cent of them) are found in homes, factories, and offices. Studies show that they usually have families, are employable, and often have exceptional skills.[4] One survey of more than 2,000 male patients who visited nine outpatient clinics for alcoholics in different parts of the country disclosed:

1. More than 80 per cent of these patients were under 50 years of age; one of four was under 35. The average age was 41.2 years, and the greatest numbers of men were between 30 and 49.

2. More than half were married and living with their wives.

3. Three out of four were living in an established household.

4. Nine out of ten had lived in their present town for at least two years.

5. Seven out of ten had held jobs involving skills or special responsibilities.

6. Nearly 60 per cent were known to have held steady employment on one job at least three years, 25 per cent for at least ten years.[5]

Wellman and his co-workers obtained similar results in their study of 830 male former alcoholics. A large proportion of the alcoholics had occupational stability, and more than 40 per cent in the group were engaged in top-level jobs, such as management and private ownership, while only 3.4 per cent were unemployed. However, because only about 6 per cent of all alcoholics receive medical and psychological aid from hospitals, outpatient clinics, or through affiliation with Alcoholics Anonymous, neither of the above studies may be truly representative.[6]

Among industrial employees, problem drinking may go unrecognized for several years. Studies show that industrial groups usually have a significantly higher age level than male patients in hospital clinics. At a large industrial concern, the average age of male alcoholics was 47.3, and the majority were 45 years or older.[7] Similarly, at another industrial establishment, 90 per cent of the group studied was 40 years or older, and one half were 50 or older.[8]

Table 1
Estimated Number of Alcoholics and Case Rates
per 100,000 Population in the U.S., 1952-1956*

State	Number	Rate
Alabama	41,500	2,330
Arizona	22,800	3,840
Arkansas	36,800	3,450
California	597,450	6,600
Colorado	39,300	3,880
Connecticut	82,700	5,260
Delaware	13,200	5,030
Florida	99,800	4,300
Georgia	58,950	2,720
Idaho	10,450	2,820
Illinois	303,100	4,640
Indiana	105,850	3,680
Iowa	47,850	2,690
Kansas	36,050	2,630
Kentucky	67,450	3,700
Louisiana	57,350	3,230
Maine	20,600	3,530
Maryland	74,700	4,200
Massachusetts	186,850	5,340
Michigan	230,700	4,840
Minnesota	68,150	3,280
Mississippi	31,000	2,570
Missouri	128,100	4,550
Montana	15,000	3,690
Nebraska	27,500	3,000
Nevada	7,450	4,850
New Hampshire	22,650	6,030
New Jersey	232,200	6,060
New Mexico	14,750	3,270
New York	672,550	5,850
North Carolina	52,350	2,180
North Dakota	10,550	2,850
Ohio	281,050	4,620
Oklahoma	34,550	2,520
Oregon	26,600	2,380
Pennsylvania	334,150	4,530
Rhode Island	28,700	4,880
South Carolina	28,450	2,120
South Dakota	11,150	2,610
Tennessee	53,650	2,550
Texas	163,050	3,020
Utah	13,800	3,080
Vermont	7,150	2,950
Virginia	62,800	2,790
Washington	67,950	4,210
West Virginia	37,100	3,090
Wisconsin	93,600	3,830
Wyoming	2,900	1,510
United States	4,712,000**	4,520

* Calculated by the Jellinek Estimation Formula from data supplied by the National Office of Vital Statistics.
** Includes D.C. (not shown in table).

Table 2
Estimated Number of Alcoholics and Case Rates per
100,000 Adults in Twelve Largest Cities, U.S., 1950*[9]

City	Number	Rate	Rank
New York, N.Y.	349,680	1,550	8
Chicago, Ill.	291,240	1,200	11
Philadelphia, Pa.	97,680	1,730	6
Los Angeles, Cal.	108,800	1,990	3
Detroit, Mich.	70,680	1,450	9
Baltimore, Md.	32,400	1,280	10
Cleveland, Ohio	46,720	1,880	4
Washington, D.C.	42,000	1,760	5
St. Louis, Mo.	37,800	1,620	7
Boston, Mass.	45,200	2,020	2
San Francisco, Cal.	90,400	4,190	1
Pittsburgh, Pa.	31,880	1,730	6

* Calculated by the Jellinek Estimation Formula from data supplied by the National Office of Vital Statistics.

NOTES

1. Keller, M., and Efron, W., *Quart. J. Stud. Alcohol,* 16:619, 1955.
2. *Ibid.,* 19:316, 1958.
3. O'Hollaren, P. and Wellman, W. M., *Calif. Med.,* 89:129, 1958.
4. Morgan, P. S., *Industr. Med. Surg.,* 27:458, 1958.
5. Straus, R. and Bacon. S. D., *Quart. J. Stud. Alcohol,* 12:231, 1951.
6. Wellman, W. M., Maxwell, M., and O'Hollaren, P., *Ibid.,* 18:388, 1957.
7. Franco, C. S., *Industr. Med. Surg.,* 26:221, 1957.
8. Thorpe, J. J. and Perret, M.D., *A.M.A. Arch. Industr. Health,* 19:24, 1959.
9. Gelber, I., *Alcoholism in New York City* (New York: Department of Health, 1960).

3 Characteristics of the Alcoholic

WHAT MAKES AN ALCOHOLIC?

Attempts have repeatedly been made to determine a set of characteristics which might identify the prealcoholic. Fox, for instance, points out that alcoholics tend to have an extremely low frustration tolerance, feelings of isolation, a tendency to act impulsively, with hostility and rebellion, and with little ability to persevere.[1] However, although it is generally agreed that most alcoholics show evidence of dependence and emotional immaturity or instability, research in this area will have to continue before the prealcoholic can be recognized in time to prevent the full-blown disease.[2]

The medical department of a large industrial concern has developed a "Profile of Alcoholism" outlining the progressive stages of alcoholism.[3] From social drinking (1), the first stage, the individual experiences such relief from inner tension that he becomes dependent on daily alcoholic support. From dependent drinking (2), he moves into the prealcoholic phase (3), where drinks are downed hastily and on the sly to deceive others. He is a problem drinker (4) when he begins to lose control of his drinking and habitually indulges in alcoholic beverages beyond the limits of the normal drinker. He is frequently drunk in the evenings and on his days off, and his relations with family and with friends are beginning to be affected.

The problem drinker is considered to have entered the alcoholic stage (5) when he needs the morning drink to face the next day. At this point, he begins to rationalize his drinking behavior. He begins to make alibis about his alcoholic intake, indulges in solitary drinking and changes the pattern of his drinking. The onset of prolonged periods of intoxication or "benders" characterizes the chronic alcoholic (6). It is these benders that occasionally result in delirium tremens and the first hospitalization of the individual. Continued excessive drinking finally produces physical effects and may result in the development of one or more of the complicating diseases of alcoholism such as cirrhosis of the liver, peripheral neuritis, and severe malnutrition. The final phase of alcoholism, then, can be classified as organic deterioration (7).

Alcoholics are usually divided into two categories: the habitual excessive symptomatic drinker, whose condition is primarily symptomatic of a social situation; and the alcoholic addict, whose drinking has the elements of compulsion and whose condition appears to be based on an underlying psychological abnormality. Franco points out that the alcohol addict appears to travel through the various stages of alcoholism at a faster pace than the symptomatic drinker. The habitual excessive symptomatic drinker, or non-addicted alcoholic, usually requires 10 to 15 years of excessive drinking before he reaches the uncontrollable stage.

HOW TO RECOGNIZE AN ALCOHOLIC

The vast majority of alcoholics have physiologic symptoms as a result of their alcoholism and many of them must be under medical care for these symptoms. But because the alcoholic usually wishes to keep his addiction hidden, and "because of the popular misconception of the 'typical' alcoholic, physicians are failing in many cases to recognize alcoholism as the underlying cause of physical symptoms. Hence, it would seem helpful to review symptoms that characteristically arise as a result of excessive drinking."[4]

The facial appearance is the first area affected overtly. The capillaries around the conjunctiva of the eye become engorged, and a puffy, edematous appearance is noted in the skin and subcutaneous tissue of the face and forehead. In fair-skinned persons, flushing of the skin is common, with pronounced hyperemia which after a long period develops into "whiskey nose." Edema may also be observed in the nasal mucous membrane, the posterior pharynx and extending into the larynx and vocal cords—the latter causing the alcoholic's characteristic hoarseness.

Perhaps the most common form of pathologic change in the stomach is alcoholic gastritis, inflammation which is manifested by loss of appetite, frequent periods of nausea, and occasional vomiting after a drinking episode. Blood in the vomitus is often found, and evidence of irritation of the lower intestinal tract may be noted.

Alcoholic tremor is one of the most common of physical changes associated with excessive drinking, and the tremor may persist long after the patient has ceased to drink. The tremor is aggravated when the patient attempts to stop drinking; it reaches its peak intensity immediately upon complete alcohol withdrawal.[5]

The exact causes of the specific cerebral metabolic disturbances produced by alcohol withdrawal are not yet known. The manifestations suggest hyperactivity of various cerebral structures, either in the form of abnormal functional stimulation or as a release phenomenon caused by exhaustion of a governing mechanism. In any case, usually little doubt exists about the diagnosis when the physician sees the alcoholic at the termination of a prolonged bout of drinking. Along with acute tremulousness, or "the shakes," caused by motor hyperactivity, the patient suffers from severe anxiety, a markedly reduced startle threshold, insomnia, and disturbing feelings of unreality and inability to concentrate. He shows evidence of marked dehydration, as a result of the diuretic action of alcohol, and of starvation, as a result of reduced food intake, nausea, vomiting and diarrhea.[6]

In about 25 per cent of tremulous patients, hallucinations may develop within 24 hours after alcohol withdrawal, although the patients are often able to communicate coherently and even describe their hallucinatory experiences.

Delirium tremens appears to be a combination of both tremulousness and hallucinosis in their severest form. Grand mal seizures or "rum fits" may initiate this syndrome, which usually occurs after the first and before the fifth day of abstinence. Tremor is coarse and severe, and the patient cannot be diverted to reality. He constantly mutters or speaks incoherently, and he is disoriented to time, place, and person. Hallucinations are vivid and often assume the form of bizarre, usually large and fast-moving animals or animal-human combinations. Auditory delusions or hallucinations are less common and are usually in the form of threatening human voices. Associated autonomic disturbance is manifested by increased blood pressure, rapid heart action, dilatation of the pupil of the eye, and profuse perspiration. Temperature elevation also may occur, despite the absence of infection.

NOTES

1. Fox, R., in Himwich, H. E. (ed.), *Alcoholism—Basic Aspects and Treatment* (Washington, D.C.: Am. Assoc. Advancement Sc., 1957), pp. 163-172.
2. Brightman, I. J., in Hilleboe, H. E. and Larimore, G. W. (eds.), *Preventive Medicine* (Philadelphia: Saunders, 1959), pp. 572-585.
3. Franco, S. C., *Industr. Med. Surg.*, 26:221, 1957.
4. O'Hollaren, P. and Wellman, W. M., *Calif. Med.*, 89:129, 1958.
5. Fazekas, J. F., Shea, J., and Rea, E., *Int. Rec. Med.* 168:333, 1955.
6. Pannill, F. C. and Smith, J. A., *J.A.M.A.* 171:2299, 1959.

4 Profile of an Alcoholic

PSYCHOLOGICAL VULNERABILITY

Numerous investigators have attempted to establish a clear picture of the alcoholic personality and—perhaps even more important—of the prealcoholic personality. Results so far have been suggestive but inconclusive. One of the conclusions of the five-year alcoholism research program at Cornell[1] was that "alcoholism is not a single entity or disease, but a symptom associated with several illnesses or syndromes." Indeed, in one series of 161 patients studied, the "symptom" was associated with eleven different diagnostic categories, including manic-depressive reactions, poorly organized psychoneurotic psychopathic personality, rigidly organized obsessive-compulsive personality, and paranoid schizophrenia.

If the alcoholic individual cannot be described precisely, the great majority do seem to have four or five personality traits in common and from these a recognizable, albeit sketchy, profile of the alcoholic can be drawn.

Low capacity for handling tensions is the trait probably most often noted by those who work with chronic alcoholics. Anything that creates tension—anxiety, anger, hostility, frustration—appears to be the Achilles' heel of the alcoholic. For example, while studying 61 alcoholic outpatients, a team of investigators recorded such capsule clinical judgments as:

"Has a low threshold for feeling rejected."

"Has a readiness to withdraw or become disorganized in the face of frustration and adversity."

"Tends to side-step troublesome situations, makes concessions to avoid unpleasantness."

"Tends to delay or avoid decision; fears committing self in any definite course of action; vacillates."[2]

Fox and Lyon[3] point out that the extremely low tension tolerance of many alcoholics is also characteristic of the infant; when the infant experiences tension—because of hunger, for example—he demands immediate relief. Similarly, the alcoholic reacts as swiftly, and almost as passionately, when things go wrong in his life.

It has been suggested that the traits most characteristic of the alcoholic are all vestigial traces of infancy. *Dependency,* as a trait, is certainly regressive and the chronic alcoholic notoriously seeks to be taken care of, either by other people or by institutions.

Zwerling, who intensively studied a group of 46 alcoholic men, noted that his subjects tended to "lean" on people. One frankly admitted, "You might say it's a parasitic existence. I depend on my mother for everything." Many of these patients found relief for their dependency needs in Alcoholics Anonymous, one describing his feeling for the organization in this way: "We have to believe in someone stronger than ourselves to look after us and take care of us."

Alcoholics often show evidence of marked *hostility* toward those closest to them. Perhaps because they are so dependent, however, this hostile core is usually repressed. (One alcoholic patient, for instance, who consciously believed that he loved his over-strict mother, informed the investigator that, "She died of a stroke—just like Stalin.")[4] Some of the excessive guilt and remorse suffered by many alcoholics stems from the partial release of this hostility under the influence of liquor; they remember "murderous" dreams and hallucinations experienced during a drinking bout or are mortally afraid of what they *may* have done during an alcoholic blackout. Occasionally, repressed hostility actually does break out during an acute intoxication stage—one of Zwerling's patients was stopped just as he was trying to push his father out of a hotel room window. By and large, though, the behavior of an alcoholic does not appear to change radically when he is drunk. (See table.)

Egocentricity is the fourth trait frequently ascribed to the alcoholic. Characteristically, he is wrapped up in his own problems and concerns and largely indifferent to the needs of others. Even those who are outwardly sociable often remain essentially estranged from other people, emotionally separate from them. Fox and Lyon note that this egocentricity is closely akin to the primary narcissism seen in early infancy when, for the baby, recognition of his own needs and their gratification is the only reality.

In addition to possessing these particular traits, the alcoholic also shows signs of neurotic intrapsychic conflicts. At least when seen by the physician, he usually appears depressed, tense, fearful, and pessimistic. These characteristics were noted in typical capsule judgments made of individual patients:

"Has a readiness to become depressed."

"Is generally nervous, tense in manner."

"Is restless."

"Is vulnerable to real or fancied threats; generally fearful; is a worrier."

"Has feelings of inadequacy, inferiority and insecurity."

In some cases, strong feelings of depression and self-loathing can lead to suicide attempts or to "accident proneness." At least eight of Zwerling's 46 patients had definitely tried to kill themselves at one time or another and a larger number—though denying any thoughts of suicide—had been involved in dangerous and potentially self-destructive behavior.

And so the profile of the alcoholic emerges. Generally speaking, he is self-centered, dependent (but bitterly resentful of his dependency), fearful, and has difficulty in coping with the tensions of everyday life. A widely held psychoanalytic theory explains why he might easily turn to alcohol for solace: deep in the subconscious of every individual is the memory of the "magical substance" of infancy—a fluid that "magically" relieved severe tension. When, as an infant, the individual was hungry, anxious, and alone, the fluid suddenly appeared. It fed him, warmed him, and soothed his fears, all at the same time. Now, as an adult, there are very few substances that come even close to fulfilling these functions. Of these, alcohol is at once the most potent, easily accessible, and socially approved substitute available.

It is easy enough to see how psychologically vulnerable people might be motivated to use the tension-reducing properties of alcohol more frequently and in greater quantities than others. Nevertheless, certainly not all who possess these "predisposing" traits drink to excess—and of those who do, not all can be considered alcohol addicts. To explain why certain individuals, and not others, eventually lose all control over their drinking, a number of investigators insist that along with psychological vulnerability there must be a physiological vulnerability as well. Certain lesions or anomalies, they believe, must be present in the individual, either inborn or acquired through heavy alcohol intake, to produce actual addiction.

PHYSIOLOGICAL VULNERABILITY

(a) Nutritional Deficiency. One school of thought holds that enzyme deficiencies in general, and vitamin deficiencies in particular, may be involved in the craving for alcohol. Part of this theory is based on evidence from controlled studies in which animals had been given vitamin-deficient diets, followed by a choice of alcohol or water to drink. Mardones[5] and his associates were among the first to observe that certain diets —notably those deficient in vitamin B complex—increased alcohol intake in rats. They ascribed this increase in voluntary alcohol consumption to lack of a specific factor, which they termed N_1, and to thiamine deficiency. Some strains of rats were more prone than others to respond to N_1 deprivation, suggesting a genetic factor also at work.

The well-known genetotrophic theory of Williams,[6] who performed similar animal studies, placed greater stress on the importance of this genetic factor, the core of his formulation being the idea of "metabolic individuality" (largely gentically determined) which predisposes some individuals to alcoholism. Williams believes that there is a need for alcohol in certain individuals and that this need is derived from nutritional faults which, in turn, are mainly due to anomalies in their enzyme systems.

Doubts as to the validity of these nutritional theories, however, were raised by Lester and Greenberg[7] in 1952. They also administered both normal and vitamin-deficient diets to experimental rats; but instead of offering only two choices of fluid —water or alcohol—they added a third choice in the form of a "sweet" solution, sucrose, and later, saccharine. Because a number of the vitamin-deprived rats preferred to ease their physical discomforts with the sweet liquid rather than the alcoholic one, the idea of a distinct physiological craving for alcohol was somewhat weakened—at least in rats.

(b) Brain Pathology. Encephalographic studies made during the last ten years indicate that some brain damage may result from heavy alcohol intake. Tumarkin and his co-workers,[8] for instance, who found evidence of cerebral cortical atrophy in seven fairly young male alcoholics, theorized that repeated, severe intoxication may result in permanent and perhaps cumulative loss of cells and nerve fibers in the cerebral cortex. This could then lead to loss of tolerance for alcohol and to psychological changes, such as impoverished powers of judgment, which would result in eventual inability to control drinking. In 1956, Lemere[9] suggested that excessive use of alcohol not only damages cortical cells but changes the metabolic pattern of brain cells so that the presence of alcohol becomes necessary for optimal brain functioning. Sudden withdrawal of alcohol then throws the brain cells into disequilibrium which brings about a cellular craving for alcohol.

(c) Endocrinological Disfunction. Endocrine disturbances are often mentioned as possible forerunners of alcoholism. J. J. Smith[10] carried out one of the first thorough clinical surveys on the endocrine aspects of alcoholism. This led him to the belief that an underlying metabolic disturbance—involving interactions of the pituitary, adrenal, and gonadal systems—preceded alcohol addiction. The outstanding feature of the alcoholic's disturbed metabolic pattern, according to Smith, is exhaustion of the adrenal, which is secondary to a pituitary deficiency. Other investigators have also noted adrenal anomalies in some chronic alcoholics.

Whether or not these or other physiological factors render one individual more susceptible to alcohol addiction than another has not yet been proved. Those who believe that only psychological stresses lead to alcoholism argue that the physiological anomalies so far uncovered are *end products* of excessive alcohol intake rather than causes. Those in the physiological camp point out that psychological stresses may lead to excessive drinking but that these stresses cannot explain loss of control, craving, and withdrawal symptoms.

A good many investigators would take the middle road and hold that both psychological and physiological vulnerability must be present to produce true alcohol addiction. As Lovell suggests:

The alcoholic is afflicted with a neurosis plus a sensitivity to alcohol. The sensitivity is the physical basis of his disease; without it his neurosis will not lead to compulsive drinking. On the other hand, the sensitivity in the absence of a neurosis probably will make an abstainer rather than an alcoholic.[11]

The Alcoholic When Drinking—Behavioral Tendencies
(in order of importance) *

Behavioral items	Alcoholic ranks himself	Informant ranks alcoholic
1. I feel guilty about what I'm doing	1	1
2. I say angry or insulting things to some people	4	2
3. I spend a lot of money or give things away	3	3
4. I just want to be by myself	2	7
5. I cry or feel very sad	5	4
6. I look for somebody to talk to and tell my troubles to	8	6
7. I like people to take care of me	10	5
8. I like to be the center of attraction	9	9
9. I want to have sexual intercourse	6.5	13
10. I find myself attracted to persons of the opposite sex	6.5	15
11. I become silly or clown around	11.5	10
12. I offer to fight somebody	14	8
13. I hurt myself by accident or intentionally	11.5	11
14. I get into scraps or fights	15	12
15. I destroy, break, or harm objects	13	14
16. I take off my clothes or exhibit myself	17	16
17. I find myself attracted to persons of the same sex	16	17

* In the study by Korman and Stubblefield of 61 outpatients, each patient—and an outside informant, usually a friend or relative—was asked to indicate the degree to which he showed each of 17 behavioral tendencies when drinking. The investigators found no dramatic change in the alcoholic's behavior from what they would have expected from his personal make-up.

NOTES

1. M. J. Sherfey, in O. Diethelm, *Etiology of Chronic Alcoholism* (Springfield, Ill.: Charles C. Thomas, 1955).

2. M. Korman and R. L. Stubblefield, *J.A.M.A.*, 178:1184, 1961.

3. R. Fox and P. Lyon, *Alcoholism—Its Scope, Cause and Treatment* (New York: Random House, 1955).

4. I. Zwerling, *Quart. J. Stud. Alcohol*, 20:543, 1959.

5. R. J. Mardones, *Quart. J. Stud. Alcohol* 12:563, 1951.

6. R. J. Williams, *Alcoholism, the Nutritional Approach* (Austin: University of Texas Press, 1959).

7. D. Lester and L. Greenberg, *Quart. J. Stud. Alcohol*, 13:553, 1952.

8. B. Tumarkin, J. D. Wilson, and G. Snyder, *U.S. Armed Forces M.J.*, 6:67, 1955.

9. F. Lemere, *Am. J. Psychiat.*, 113:361, 1956.

10. J. J. Smith, *Quart. J Stud. Alcohol*, 10:251, 1949.

11. H. W. Lovell, *Hope and Help for the Alcoholic* (Garden City, N.Y.: Doubleday, 1951).

5 The "Intelligent" Alcoholic—Why Does He Drink?

"I drink," states one kind of alcoholic patient, "because I am more creative, more intelligent—and therefore more high-strung—than other people. Alcohol gives me the stimulation I need to cope with the mediocrity that surrounds me." The belief that the creative person has greater need to insulate his "sensitive" nerves with alcohol is a popular one. And while it is true that a good many alcoholics are both dullards and thick-skinned, perhaps just as many alcoholics have been brilliant enough to achieve a considerable measure of success in life.

In his *Cup of Fury*, for instance, Upton Sinclair[1] discusses a tragically long list of friends and acquaintances who, directly or indirectly, destroyed themselves through excessive drinking:

William Sidney Porter (O. Henry) had to be sobered up before he could write many of his famous short stories. Stephen Crane, after falling ill in Cuba, took to drinking heavily as a "cure" and was dead at 29. Eugene V. Debs was a fiery orator and a truly gentle soul but a captive of alcohol.

47

"When Gene went on lecture tours, he was accompanied by a strong man whose major duty was to keep him fit to go on the platform." Sinclair Lewis ended a brilliant career by drinking a quart of brandy a day, wandering over the earth, avoiding his friends, and desperately seeking peace. Maxwell Bodenheim, a handsome, striking man when young and author of several best-selling novels, spent his last few years wandering through Greenwich Village, posing as a blind man to pick up some coins or offering to write "poetry" for tourists in return for a drink. Hart Crane, a confirmed and hopeless alcoholic at 33, dove from a steamer into the Caribbean sea. Ambrose Bierce, a heavy-drinking and tormented man, wandered off into Mexico, which was then aflame with war and banditry, and died in a manner unreported and still unknown. F. Scott Fitzgerald wasted so much of his life on alcohol that he was known to his friends as "F. Scotch Fitzgerald." Sinclair mentions others as well—Edna St. Vincent Millay, Eugene O'Neill Finley Peter Dunne, George Sterling, William Seabrook, Sherwood Anderson, John Barrymore, Douglas Fairbanks, Sr., Isidora Duncan—all enormously talented and successful people who nevertheless spent a good part of their days as victims of alcoholism.

SUICIDE BY INCHES

It sometimes seems as if the alcohol addict is deliberately bent on destroying himself, on alienating his family and friends, on ruining his career and his reputation. And, in view of Karl Menninger,[2] chronic alcoholism should actually be termed chronic suicide—that form of self-destruction in which individuals commit suicide by inches.

Certainly, alcoholics are preoccupied, even in their sober moments, with thoughts of self-destruction in which individuals commit suicide by inches.

Certainly, alcoholics are preoccupied, even in their sober moments, with thoughts of self-destruction. Jack London,[3] for instance, who described his struggles with alcohol in the book *John Barleycorn,* observed that "suicide, quick or slow, a sudden spill or a gradual oozing away, is the price John Barleycorn exacts. No friend of his ever escapes making the just due payment." And though London promised at the end of this book, "I will drink, but, oh, more skillfully, more discreetly than ever before. Never again will I be a peripatetic conflagration," he continued to drink as recklessly as before and, in less than three years, took his own life.

Other alcoholics prefer the less overt form of suicide. Like Dylan Thomas, they simply continue to drink in the full knowledge that they are endangering their lives. J. M. Brinnin, who accompanied Thomas on his lecture tours of the United States, reports that the famous Welsh poet drank steadily despite occasional attacks of coughing followed by severe retching and vomiting. "I think I have cirrhosis of the liver," the poet informed Brinnin after one of these attacks, but he refused to cut down on his drinking. Significantly, one of the last things he said before going into a fatal alcoholic coma was, "I want to go to the Garden of Eden—to die . . . to be forever unconscious."[4]

Both Lillian Roth and Diana Barrymore also continued to drink after being warned that it might mean their deaths. Lillian Roth heard a medical verdict of impending blindness, the onset of cirrhosis, advanced colitis, and a form of alcoholic insanity. Despite this, she continued to drink for several years, at one point crying, "I've got to finish the bottle. I don't care what happens, I've got to finish the bottle. I want death."[5] Fortunately, with help, Miss Roth eventually managed to shake free from her addiction. Diana Barrymore, however, heard roughly the same verdict from her doctor. "You're on a dreadful merry-go-round—alcohol, barbiturates, stimulants. If you don't get off it quickly, you will die."[6] Despite a desperate struggle and occasional success, the actress never really managed to get off that merry-go-round. She died at the age of 38.

Why did these and other highly intelligent people become addicted to alcohol? Each person might have offered a different excuse. But according to Karl Menninger, the alcoholic suffers secretly from an unspeakable terror which he cannot bear to face. Further, whatever excuse he may give he often doesn't know the actual nature of the dreadful pain and fear within him which impels him to alcoholic self-destruction.

Menninger suggests, then, that alcohol addiction is not a disease, but rather a suicidal flight *from* disease, a disastrous attempt at the self-cure of an unseen inner conflict. It stems from the underlying feeling of insecurity that grips even the outwardly successful alcoholic, and it is this feeling that must constantly be denied, compensated for, or anesthetized.

The "outward success" is particularly vulnerable when he fears that his creative powers are starting to fade. F. Scott Fitzgerald apparently had begun drinking as a young man because in those days, he said, everyone drank. He enjoyed life in those days, however, and felt that all he needed to make a living was pencil and paper. "But then I found I needed liquor, too," he told a friend. "I needed it to write."[7] He began to drink more and more to escape the growing sense of his wasted potentiality and also to escape strong feelings of guilt concerning his young wife, who had become insane.

William Seabrook described the feelings of a frustrated writer in his autobiography, *No Hiding Place*. "I was miserable . . . and before I knew it, I was drinking again in the mornings when I didn't want to drink, not for the pleasure but in the desperate false hope that I might write a page or two that wasn't wooden."[8]

Judging from their writings, the pattern of alcoholism for

these creative people is the familiar one: strong feelings of inferiority even as a child; drinking begun because socially it seems "the thing to do"; the passage of several years before alcohol really takes hold. Diana Barrymore might have been speaking for any number of female alcoholics when she wrote, "As a child I'd been around clever, cultured people, but I never felt part of them. The few times I came downstairs to meet mother's famous literary friends, I'd felt . . . frightened and an imposter. . . . Now the same sense of inadequacy swept over me. Trying to be what people expected, I reached for the quip . . . A few drinks helped things along."

Jack London, like many alcoholics, admitted that he never liked the taste of alcohol. But in his youth, he found that saloons were desirable places, bright and cheerful, full of warmth and good fellowship. It was after years of social drinking that he found he *had* to drink. "I was carrying a beautiful alcoholic conflagration around with me. The thing fed on its own heat and flamed the fiercer. There was no time in all my waking time that I didn't want to drink."

For most alcoholics, the amount of liquor that must be consumed appears to grow steadily. At first, Lillian Roth observes, beer by day and liquor by night satisfied her. But then her nerves seemed to demand more and she switched from a morning beer to two ounces of bourbon in her morning orange juice. This satisfied her for a while, but one morning, while out shopping with a friend, she had a dizzy spell and almost collapsed. The friend hurried her to a cab and the experienced driver, taking one look at her, advised a quick drink. "Take a tip," he advised her, "and carry a shot or two with you in the future."

Miss Roth realized then that the physical demand was growing, that it was dangerous for her even to leave the house without carrying an emergency supply of liquor with her. That day, she bought some two-ounce medicine bottles in the drug store, filled them with liquor, and thereafter was never without a couple in her purse.

The two-ounce bottles gradually became full-sized fifths. After years of steadily increasing consumption, additional punishment for the desperately sick woman came, inevitably, in the form of "the shakes" with its concomitant physical agony. She was in constant pain—in the eyes, nose, throat, sinuses, head, chest, stomach, legs—and only liquor could relieve it, but her body rejected liquor. "After the shakes, of course, came delirium tremens."

Yet, despite the physical and mental torture the alcoholic suffers, he continues to drink. And one reason for this, Menninger suggests, is because his deep feelings of inferiority, sinfulness, and unworthiness lead him naturally to think of suicide. When the individual is threatened with destruction by his own impulses, he may choose alcoholism as a kind of lesser self-destruction serving to avert the greater self-destruction.

These feelings of inferiority, in this psychiatrist's view, are based on fear and guilt induced by the feelings of rage, frustration, envy, or hostility the individual experienced as a child.

All children meet with frustration and disappointment which cause them to have ambivalent feelings toward their parents. With an alcoholic, however, there apparently is a qualitative difference. The disappointments he suffers as a child become more than he can bear. His suffering is so great that he remains all his life an "oral character," never completely outgrowing that stage in his psychological development in which the child's attitude toward the world is determined by his wish to take it in through the mouth and to destroy with his mouth anything which resists his demands.

To punish loved ones by eating and drinking—or by not eating and drinking—is a typical infantile revenge reaction. Since the alcoholic suffers conflicting feelings of love and hate toward his family because of early disappointments, real and imaginary, he wants to punish them. But, at the same time, he feels guilty about his desires. Alcoholism, therefore, serves many purposes: it is a passive form of aggression toward others; it punishes the individual for his own repressed hostilities; and it keeps him from the even greater self-punishment of *total* self-destruction.

NOTES

1. U. Sinclair, *The Cup of Fury* (Great Neck, New York: Channel Press, 1956).
2. K. A. Menniger, *Man Against Himself* (New York: Harcourt Brace, 1938).
3. J. London, *John Barleycorn* (New York: D. Appleton-Century, 1938).
4. J. M. Brinnin, *Dylan Thomas in America* (Boston: Little, Brown, 1955).
5. L. Roth, *I'll Cry Tomorrow* (New York: Frederick Fell, 1954).
6. D. Barrymore and G. Frank, *Too Much, Too Soon* (New York: Henry Holt, 1957).
7. S. Graham and G. Frank, *Beloved Infidel* (New York: Henry Holt, 1958).
8. W. Seabrook, *No Hiding Place*, in Sinclair, *op. cit.*

6 The Craving for Alcohol

DEPENDENCE AND DESIRE

The craving for alcohol, "an urgent and overpowering desire to drink alcoholic beverages,"[1] is of a twofold nature. For physical reasons—biochemical and physiologic in nature—the chronic alcoholic apparently "needs" alcohol to relieve withdrawal symptoms. No clearly evident physical reasons exist, however, to explain the alcoholic's sudden irresistible desire for liquor after a long period of abstinence. Here, psychological factors seem to dominate. Because different mechanisms are involved in the two cravings, the World Health Organization (WHO) labels the end-of-bout craving a physical dependence on alcohol, the between-bout craving a pathological desire for alcohol.

(a) Physical Dependence. Are alcoholics physically dependent upon alcohol to the extent that they can be considered true addicts? The severity of withdrawal symptoms, sometimes "more dangerous to the life of the individual than are any of the manifestations of withdrawal of morphine,"[2] would certainly indicate a true physical dependence. However, alcohol is not by law an addicting drug.

Unlike those who use morphine or other narcotic drugs (of whom 70 to 100 per cent can be considered physically addicted), the great majority of persons who drink alcohol remain largely unaffected. Alcohol consumption, in fact, appears to lead to some form of dependency in a maximum of only 10 per cent, and this dependency requires heavy and excessive use of the drug over a long period of time—usually from three to 20 years.[3] The WHO Committee on Alcohol and Alcoholism, therefore, considers ethyl alcohol a drug "intermediate in kind and degree" between habit-forming drugs and addiction-producing drugs. They point out that, while "compulsive craving" and "dependence upon alcohol" can develop and can manifest themselves in severe withdrawal symptoms, these processes occur in only a relatively small number of users.

Although acquired tolerance to alcohol has been demonstrated in long-term drinkers—as well as a cross tolerance to certain anesthetics such as ether and choloroform—very little is known concerning the biochemical and neurophysiologic mechanisms responsible for withdrawal symptoms. During the withdrawal stage, the alcoholic appears to be chiefly interested in relieving the distressing withdrawal symptoms by the ingestion of alcohol. Demand for alcohol frequently ceases if the symptoms are controlled with other drugs.[4] After a period of abstinence, the alcoholic (unless he has incurred gastritis, cirrhosis, or other conditions associated with escessive drinking) usually appears physiologically normal.[5] Yet he relapses.

(b) Pathological Desire. The alcoholic's sudden craving for alcohol after a period of abstinence has been attributed either to some acquired or inherited metabolic defect or else to psychological factors. Theories have been advanced by those in favor of the first approach relating the craving to nutritional or biochemical deficiencies, to endocrine disorders, to brain pathology, or to an allergy of some kind. While most investigators can present evidence to support their views, it is generally agreed that much more research is needed in this area. After studying the existing hypotheses, the WHO Committee concludes only that "a physiopathological condition (other than physical dependence) cannot be excluded as one of the factors" involved in this between-bout craving.

The Committee believes that psychological factors make the most important contribution to the development of this craving, noting:

During a period of abstinence, even in the absence of withdrawal symptoms, one observes clinically the building up of psychological tension which provokes a pathological desire for alochol as a means of relieving this tension; in this condition, the individual may be said to be psychologically dependent on alcohol.

While in a relatively small group of alcoholics this pathological desire is evident at the start of the drinking career, the majority of alcoholics require several years of excessive drinking to build up either physical or psychological dependencies.

This excessive drinking is usually due to a combination of cultural and psychological factors. Many persons find that the use of alcohol, because it satisfies the deep-seated psychological need for relief from the tension induced by anxieties, frustrations, and conflicts, easily tends to become habitual. The habit of regularly consuming large quantities of alcohol then becomes so fixed that—perhaps in connection with physical changes brought about by prolonged excessive drinking—it can be experienced as a strong craving for alcohol.[6]

Whether a given person can resist this strong craving depends, by and large, on his personality. The craving in someone "with psychopathy who is sensitive . . . often suffers from anxiety and who has experienced that alcohol is very effective in alleviating his troubles" is quite different from the craving "in a well-adjusted personality . . . relatively well organized and with a better tolerance for anxiety."

The sensitive and anxious alcoholic, at least, will almost

certainly need medical and psychological help if he is to combat both his physical and psychological cravings. With today's
new and effective methods of treatment, his chances are substantially better than ever before.

PHYSIOLOGY OF THE HANGOVER

If alcohol withdrawal symptoms afflict relatively few who
drink, the same can hardly be said of the hangover. Almost
everyone who has downed a substantial number of drinks has
experienced, the morning after, some variation of the following: "vomiting, loss of appetite, heartburn, lassitude, continued thirst, tremors of head and limbs, palpitation, weakness
of joints, respiratory difficulties, sleeplessness, giddiness and a
feeling as if one were wrapped in a sheet." This classic description occurs in ancient Hindu ayurvedic medicine and was
written at least 2500 years ago. Although centuries of suffering
have since elapsed, the cause of the hangover is still not definitely known. The associated symptoms, however, are presumably either reactions or counter-reactions to the physiologic
effects of alcohol.

The most marked of these effects is on the central nervous
system. Because alcohol first depresses the higher mental processes,[7] a few drinks can dull the individual's judgment,
memory, concentration, and insight. By reducing self-criticism,
the drinks help to remove inhibitions, so that the man who is
"high" acts and speaks impulsively and with greater-than-
normal self-confidence. Since alcohol also raises the pain
threshold, the celebrant, finding himself happily immune to
minor aches and pains, remains active long past the stage of
neuromuscular exhaustion—which overactivity partly explains
the overwhelming fatigue of the next day.

Another reason for this fatigue is that, while alcohol raises
the blood sugar level during drinking, several hours later the

level can drop to at least 19 per cent below normal.[8] Both this hypoglycemia and the strenuous overactivity of the previous evening may be principal causes of the sufferer's throbbing headache, as well. Other possibilities are an accumulation of acetaldehyde in the system,[9] or an allergy either to the grains involved in alcohol production or to the congeners that give each liquor its characteristic flavor and aroma.[10]

Perhaps the most universal hangover symptom is an intense and prolonged thirst. Numerous investigators have established alcohol's diuretic effect, which appears to result from inhibition of the supraoptico-hypophyseal system, leading to decreased secretion of the antidiuretic hormone.[11],[12] In addition to fluids lost through urination, perspiration, and vomiting, disturbances in the body's fluid balance, with water in the cells shifting to the extracellular spaces, can give the individual a sensation of thirst no matter how much liquid he tries to consume.

Digestive upsets are common in the hangover phase; that they are is hardly surprising. Ethyl alcohol is extremely irritating to the mucosa, even in the 50 per cent concentration of 100 proof whiskey. Most drinkers dilute their beverages, of course, and this dilution, plus the presence of food in the stomach, offers some protection. But since one or two drinks stimulate excessive and highly acid gastric secretion, irritation is rarely escaped. The consumption of several drinks gradually slows down, or even stops, digestive activity. The next morning, therefore, the individual finds that he is nauseated, has a queasy stomach, and little or no appetite.

Other physiological actions of alcohol which may produce unpleasant aftereffects are the depression of the body metabolism of serotonin and other monoamines concerned with cerebral metabolism, increased secretion of epinephrine and levarterenol, stimulation of the vomiting center,[13] and disturbance of the vestibular system. Emotional factors such as guilt and remorse may play an important role in hangover misery as well.

Treatment of the hangover is symptomatic and usually includes the use of analgesics, sedatives, anti-emetics, fluids and nourishment.

NOTES

1. Mardones, J., *Quart. J. Stud. Alcohol*, 16:51, 1955.
2. WHO Techn. Rep. Ser., No. 94: "Alcohol and Alcoholism" (Geneva, 1955).
3. Jellinek, E. M., The Disease Concept of Alcoholism (New Haven: Hillhouse, 1960), pp. 33ff.
4. Jellinek, E. M., *Quart. J. Stud. Alcohol*, 16:35, 1955.
5. Isbell, H.: *ibid.*, p. 38.
6. Lundquist, G.: *ibid.*, p. 42.
7. Goodman, L. S. and Gilman, A., *The Pharmaceutical Basis of Therapeutics* (New York: Macmillan, ed. 2, 1955), pp. 98ff.
8. Vartia, O. K., Forsander, O. A., and Krusius, F., *Quart. J. Stud. Alcohol,* 21:597, 1960.
9. Himwich, H. E., in Thompson, G. N. (ed.), *Alcoholism* (Springfield, Ill.: Thomas, 1956), pp. 291ff.
10. Damrau, F. and Liddy, E., *J. Nat. Med. Assoc.,* 52:262, 1960.
11. Rubini, M. E., Kleeman, C. R., and Lamdin, E., *J. Clin. Invest.,* 34:439, 1955.
12. Kleeman, C. R., Rubini, M. E., Lambdin, E., and Epstein, F. H., *ibid.,* p. 448.
13. Nimz, R. A., *J.A.M.A.,* 177:96, 1961.

In societies which have a low degree of acceptance of large daily amounts of alcohol, mainly those will be exposed to the risk of addiction who on account of high psychological vulnerability have an inducement to go against the social standards. But in societies which have an extremely high degree of acceptance of large daily alcohol consumption, the presence of any small vulnerability, whether psychological or physical, will suffice for exposure to the risk of addiction.[1]

7 The Sociology of Alcoholism

From the German beer hall to the English pub, from the Frenchman and his apéritif to the American cocktail party, the custom of drinking is a tradition which has long occupied a prominent place in many cultures of the world. Even Hippocrates recognized the value of alcohol in making his patients "feel better." As a negative outgrowth of this custom, however, developed the ever-increasing problem of alcoholism, fourth among the nation's health problems, outranked only by mental illness, heart disease, and cancer. There are well over five million alcoholics in the U.S. today.[2]

Alcoholism, complex and unresolved problem that it is, cannot be traced to any specific milieu, but is found in every walk of life, on every level of society, and in all economic circumstances. Alcoholism seems to be more prevalent among the lowest and highest social strata.[3] At any rate, the higher economic and educational levels include a greater over-all number of drinkers (not necessarily alcoholics).

The number of drinkers increases roughly with the size of the community population. Urban areas, where the style seems to be set, exhibit a higher incidence of drinking than rural areas. Studies report that 46 per cent of the adult population drink in rural areas as contrasted with 77 per cent in the largest cities. Perhaps the stresses and strains of an urban society and its structure, per se, are more conducive to individual maladjustment. In addition, cities seem to attract deviant personalities from the more rigid rural societies.[4] However, the constant change of environmental factors in our dynamic society is reflected by a gradual shift occurring in this urban-rural ratio.

Because the individual is highly susceptible to group pressures, social attitudes are significant in the incidence of drinking and alcoholism. Individual drinking patterns tend to follow more closely those of the peer group than those of the previous generations.[5] The custom of drinking, one of America's leading social forms, has become a habit in both leisure and business hours. Acceptance of daily low or high alcoholic intake determines, in part, the exposure to the risk of alcoholism. For the person who attempts to abstain where drinking is the rule, social pressure stands ready to challenge will power and determination. Being sober while others drink is both difficult and perturbing. The abstainer cannot help feeling different and uneasy. If he succeeds in not conforming to the drinking in progress, a greater discomfort awaits him: he is no longer welcome because he does not seem "sociable" any more.

Economic factors make a noteworthy contribution to the prevailing social attitudes. The slum dweller often favors the atmosphere of the tavern over his drab home environment. The cost relationship between alcohol and staple foods and, at times, economic self-interest (as in wine-growing regions) also influence the rate of consumption of alcohol and the incidence of alcoholism. For example, a daily intake of two quarts of wine is not unusual in France, although it is very high by American standards.

Drinking behavior is often best explained in terms of cultural traits. In the fixed societies of Europe, drinking followed a traditional pattern with little or no change over long periods of time. In the fluid American society, however, former cultural traits are gradually obliterated as the individual ethnic groups move closer to the average. For Scandinavian-Americans, for example, who originally had high rates, the rate of consumption is decreasing, whereas for Italian-Americans the rate is increasing. The highest rates of alcoholism in the United States are among the Irish-American group; Poles and native white Americans also have high rates of alcoholism. The Italians and Greeks have low rates, while the Jewish group shows not only the lowest rate of alcoholism but also a high rate of consumption. The low rates of alcoholism among the Italians, Greeks, and Jews might best be explained by the use of alcoholic beverages primarily in the home as social and religious rituals.

Occupations which make it difficult to maintain family and community life or those concerned with the alcohol industry—such as bartenders, nightclub entertainers, and liquor salesmen—report a high rate of alcoholism.[6] However, alcoholism is not limited to any one category, but is found in a variety of professions and fields. One of the most alarming examples is the housewife and mother who becomes an alcoholic. Recent figures estimate the rising incidence of alcoholism in women as one-fifth to one-third of all alcoholics.[7] By the very nature of their lives, many of these sad cases, afraid to be found out, have remained hidden away and are only now coming out of confinement to seek medical assistance.

THE ALCOHOLIC—HIS FAMILY AND FRIENDS

The symptoms of alcoholism are noticed first by those closest to the alcoholic, usually members of his family. At this time, the family not uncommonly makes the bitter mistake of being hostile to and critical of him, thus helping to perpetuate, in large measure, his need to pursue the alcoholic avenue of escape. Rather than sympathetically looking for his hidden motives and taking an objective view of him, family members often share his distorted view of himself and so force him deeper into alcoholism.

Although the alcoholic may manage to keep his marriage alive and to hold a job, closer inspection reveals much emotional chaos in his home life. When the family's help and encouragement would be of greatest value to him, he often meets their condemnation and scorn. With low tolerance of frustration and deep feelings of inadequacy, he soon centers his life around the bottle. And as he stands aside, watching his family sink or swim in spite of him, resentment and indifference increase.

Many wives of alcoholics demonstrate serious neurotic tendencies. When given the opportunity to divorce their mates or to place them in treatment hospitals, they often refuse. Today, drunkenness is recognized as grounds for divorce in some 40 states. In many instances where the woman is the alcoholic, the family has very carefully hidden her from the condemning eyes of society, only to speed her progress down the pathway of alcoholism. In either case, many alcoholics are shocked into positive action only by the threat of a complete separation from family or of divorce.

In the early stages of the disease, the alcoholic still may be accepted by his friends, who kindly regard each drinking episode as an exception or completely overlook it. Feeling remorse, the alcoholic drinks again to relax his tension and his apprehension. Soon a pattern develops. As he continues to gulp down his drinks, he realizes that he is becoming less proficient in his work. Unable to view the process from any but the most self-centered point of view, he seeks refuge in grandiose rhetoric and plans for the future, while his realistic accomplishment diminishes. His friends, increasingly aware of his drinking, may try to talk to him about it, but to no avail. Sensing his loss of popularity, the alcoholic drops old group affiliations, avoids old and true friends, and makes and loses new ones in rapid succession in his downward progress to severe alcoholism.

As more and more information, treatment, and rehabilitation centers are being established across the nation, the alcoholic and his family find greater assistance and understanding. Emphasis on alcoholism as a disease has done much toward bringing the alcoholic to the attention of the physician at an earlier stage of his disease. Alcoholics Anonymous and Al Anon Family Groups are making large strides forward in helping the alcoholic himself, as well as the four or five other persons involved in each case, better to understand and overcome the difficulties and problems on the road to successful rehabilitation.

NOTES

1. Jellinek, E. M., *The Disease Concept of Alcoholism* (New Haven: Hillhouse, 1950), pp. 28-29.
2. Mann, M., paper read at Annual Meeting, National Council on Alcoholism, Salt Lake City, 1959.
3. Bacon, S. D., *Alcoholism: Nature of the Problem;* and *Alcoholism: Its Extent, Therapy, Prevention* (New York: National Council on Alcoholism).
4. Fox, R. and Lyon, P., *Alcoholism: Its Scope, Cause and Treatment* (New York: Random House, 1955), pp. 12ff.
5. Haer, J. L., *Quart. J. Stud. Alcohol,* 16:178, 1955.
6. Kant, F., *The Treatment of the Alcoholic* (Springfield, Ill.: Thomas, 1954), pp. 8-16, 29-34, 37-47.
7. Golin, M., *J.A.M.A.* 167:1496, 1958.

8 The Alcoholic Female

For the nearly one million female alcoholics in this country, drinking tends to be a lonely and hidden affair. Because society judges the intoxicated female more harshly than it does the male, the woman who drinks to excess often does so in the privacy of her home.[1] Thus, many female alcoholics may go to bed at night with a bottle, or sip at one surreptitiously throughout the day.[2] Housewives in particular have an excellent opportunity for unobserved and continuous drinking, and a large number of alcoholic housewives are able to hide their condition for much longer periods than the working male usually can.

This tendency toward secret drinking leads some authorities to believe that the generally accepted ratio—one female alcoholic to every five or six males in the United States[3]—may be too low. Certainly there seems to have been a rise in the number of women who drink, particularly since the war years. Riley and Marden in their 1946 national survey of public attitudes toward alcohol, found that 75 per cent of the male population are drinkers as against 56 per cent of the female population. Comparing this with a 1940 survey, they noted not only a sharp rise in the incidence of drinking among both men and women, but a narrowing of the gap between the sexes as well, apparently "in line with the general trend in our society toward less and less differentiation in the social behavior of men and women."[4]

However, while the same proportion of men and women are occasional drinkers (48 per cent), over three times as many men (27 per cent) as women (8 per cent) are regular drinkers. One "alcohol poll,"[5] which found that 76 per cent of males and 51 per cent of females drink, gives an interesting breakdown of the different drinking patterns of men and women (see Table 9).

Table 9
Drinking Frequency[6]

	% Men	% Women
Each day	7.5	0.0
4-6 times a week	4.0	1.2
3 times a week	7.9	2.0
1-2 times a week	10.1	6.1
2-3 times a month	15.9	12.7
Once a month	14.5	9.4
1-5 times a year	16.3	20.0
	76.2	51.4

Table 10
Male-Female Ratio of Alcoholism in Different Settings

Private Practice	Social Agencies	Hospitals	Police Custody
3 males	4 males	6 males	11 males
1 female	1 female	1 female	1 female

Along with the increase in female drinkers in general, the "greater rate of emergence of formerly hidden alcoholics among women"[7] leads some investigators to believe that the number of female alcoholics has risen dramatically. However, available statistics still tend to confirm the ratio of five or six males to one female. In any case, since women alcoholics appear more often in certain therapeutic settings than in others (see Table 10), physicians in private pracitce treat proportionately more female alcoholics than do other physicians, and some are treating almost an even number of men and women.

Table 11
General Social Characteristics of Alcoholic Outpatients[8]

		55 Men	46 Women
A. Age		%	%
	20-29	13	11
	30-39	34	33
	40-49	41	42
	50-59	7	11
	60-69	4	4
	Mean	39.8 years	41.3 years
B. Educational achievement		%	%
	Less than 8th grade	0	0
	Completed 8th grade, or some high school	31	31
	Completed high school	31	33
	Some college	20	26
	Completed college or beyond	18	11
C. Occupational classification*		%	%
	Business, major or minor	18	15
	Professions	9	22
	Public service, clerical, selling	22	40
	Skilled labor	22	0
	Semiskilled or unskilled labor	29	25
D. Religious background		%	%
	Roman Catholic	47	40
	Protestant	41	53
	Jewish	0	0
	Greek Orthodox	2	2
	Not ascertained	9	7

* % for women based on only 28 cases; 18 full-time housewives included.

Table 12
Home Backgrounds of Alcoholic Outpatients

	% Men	% Women
Broken home	41	42
Patients not raised by own parents	9	18
Working mother supported family	2	7
Problem drinking in parents	35	44
Problem drinking in siblings	9	24

The question then arises: do female alcoholics differ markedly from their male counterparts, and are they more difficult to treat? Some controversy surrounds the matter. There is a widely held belief that female alcoholics are more abnormal,[9] show greater personality disorganization than men, may have a "more severe degree" of alcoholism,[10] and as a result present more problems in management. However, there is little evidence to indicate that such is true of all female alcoholics or even of most. The average woman attending an alcoholism outpatient clinic is, in fact, less likely to have been a "public nuisance" than the male outpatient, and more likely to have escaped arrest and hospitalization in the past.

Aside from this, men and women outpatients of clinics for alcoholism are remarkably similar, particularly in terms of age, education, and social and cultural backgrounds. Lisansky compared a group of men and women patients attending Yale Plan and Connecticut Commission Clinics and reported the findings given in Table 11.

The 46 women subjects of Table 11 included 18 who were full-time housewives; among the others, who held full or part-time positions, there were three nurses, a schoolteacher, a social worker, and a published author, all of them "functioning more or less efficiently in their jobs." In this study, 27 per cent of the women were either separated or divorced from their husbands as compared to a norm of about 5 per cent of Connecticut women of the same ages. The number of alcoholic women married to problem-drinking spouses is also much higher than can be explained by chance expectancy: fully 35 per cent of these women reported having alcoholic husbands.

The men and women in this study were again alike in having had disruptive early home backgrounds (see Table 12). In relatively few instances did either men or women report having both parents present during childhood, or having a relaxed and affectionate family life. For the majority of the male alcoholics, the father was either absent or a strict and rejecting parent. For the women, the mother generally was considered the rejecting parent. In addition, a significantly higher proportion of the women were raised by foster families or relatives. Problem drinking in their parents was frequently mentioned.

Other etiologic factors also provide little evidence of a substantial difference between male and female alcoholics. The hypothesis of a relationship between alcoholism in women and the feminine physiological functions of menstruation, childbirth, and menopause remains unproved. Like men, women apparently began drinking for a variety of conscious reasons. Upon questioning, for instance, they may cite such factors as marital conflicts, tensions, physical complaints (including postpartum and menopausal depression), problems with children and in-laws, an unhappy love affair, or the death of a loved one. The major cause of their alcoholic episodes, as seen by one group of married patients, lay in the relationship with the spouse; violent quarrels, reactions to his drinking, loneliness caused by his deliberate or enforced absences, all induced the wife to turn to alcohol for solace.[11]

Quite often, a spouse becomes alcoholic in order to keep the drinking partner company but, paradoxically, while the wife may accept her husband as a "drinking male," the husband is much less tolerant of his wife's excessive drinking. Alcoholic episodes are therefore often triggered by "the husband's own drinking as well as his non-constructive attitude towards the wife's drinking."[12]

While men and women alcoholics may drink excessively because of similar early family difficulties or similar conflicts, the patterns of their drinking do differ slightly. Of the alcoholics in the Lisansky study, the men took their first drink at a significantly earlier average age (17.0) than the women (20.8), and appeared at the clinic with longer histories of problem drinking (12.3 years) than the women (9.8 years). However, there also appears to be a tendency for more "plateau drinking" among women—drinking to the point of dulling the edges of reality but not enough to hamper function—particularly in the case of "sipping" housewives. Perhaps the major difference in the drinking patterns of men and women is that men do much of their drinking in company, that is, at parties and at bars and taverns, while women alcoholics tend to drink alone and at home.

MATERNAL ALCOHOLISM

The woman alcoholic's problems become unique, of course, when she is pregnant. Maternal alcoholism in itself actually appears to have no effect on the fetus; however, its two most obvious dangers—nutritional inadequacy and accidental injuries—make treatment of the condition essential. A gradual withdrawal of alcohol must be urged and, if alcoholism presents an acute and serious problem during pregnancy or labor, appropriate calming and sedating agents can be administered. Fortunately, cirrhosis is rarely associated with pregnancy, in part because the disease generally develops in an older age group and in part because it apparently impairs fertility in younger patients. The few reported experiences indicate that a compensated cirrhotic—a patient without unusual symptoms and with laboratory evidence of fairly good liver function—can tolerate pregnancy well and be reasonably assured of a healthy infant. However, careful supervision under hospital conditions may be required and, in some extreme cases, therapeutic abortion.[13]

If the woman alcoholic presents few complications unique to her sex except during pregnancy, she does have one additional distinction: alcoholism in women almost always produces greater disruption in family life than alcoholism in men.

A child, after all, may be somewhat shielded from a drunken father, but rarely from a drunken mother. Therefore, one of the most vital needs in further alcoholism research is a means of identifying alcoholic females, and particularly "concealed, early-stage alcoholic women who drink at home,"[14] so that they can be treated.

NOTES

1. Fox, R. and Eisenstein, W. W. (eds.), *Neurotic Interaction in Marriage* (New York: Basic Books, 1956), chap. 9.
2. Lisansky, E. S., *Quart. J. Stud. Alcohol*, 18:588, 1957.
3. Keller, M. and Efron, V., *ibid.*, 16:619, 1955.
4. Riley, J. W., Jr., and Marden, C. F., *ibid.*, 8:265, 1947.
5. Maxwell, M. A. *ibid.*, 13:219, 1952.
6. Chicago Committee on Alcoholism, "Survey of Alcoholism, 1955," *ibid.*, 16:619, 1955. Both tables from same source.
7. Keller and Efron, *loc. cit.*
8. Lisansky, *loc. cit.* Both tables.
9. Karpman, B., *The Alcoholic Women* (Washington, D.C.: Linacre Press, 1948).
10. Spain, D. M., *Amer. J. Clin. Path.*, 15:215, 1945.
11. Rosenbaum, B., *Quart. J. Stud. Alcohol*, 19:79, 1958.
12. *Ibid.*
13. Guttmacher, A. F. and Rovinsky, J. J. (eds), *Medical, Surgical and Gynecological Complications in Pregnancy* (Baltimore: Williams & Wilkins, 1960), pp. 195ff., 382.
14. Lisansky, *loc. cit.*

9 Problem Drinking and the Community

SOCIAL COSTS OF ALCOHOLISM

For the year 1940, it was estimated that at least $778,903,000 was spent in the United States as a result of the excessive use of alcohol.[1] Today, excessive drinking undoubtedly costs the American public well over a billion dollars each year, with part of the bill borne by industry, the rest by a myriad of social, charitable, religious, and governmental agencies. Thus, even if one ignores such immeasurable personal losses as happiness, love, dignity, and self-respect, alcoholism remains one of the country's most expensive diseases—and one that, in every community, creates or intensifies problems in several important areas.

As a *threat to public health*, for instance, alcoholism stands fourth among leading health problems in the United States, outranked only by heart disease, cancer, and mental illness. There are over five million alcoholics whose health is directly damaged by excessive drinking and who, at one time or another, require treatment of the medical problems created by excessive drinking, such as acute intoxication, withdrawal symptoms, coma, gastritis, and cirrhosis of the liver. Some develop a psychosis as a complication of their alcoholism. In New York State, alcoholics with psychosis have made up about 8 per cent of all first admissions to state hospitals.[2]

Since chronic alcoholism is a protracted disorder, many alcoholics who eventually do resolve their drinking problems may not do so for years after first seeking treatment. In the interval, general practitioners, specialists, and hospital personnel may be called on repeatedly to deal with conditions resulting from the patient's use of alcohol. Not surprisingly, then, in most communities the psychiatric and medical agencies presently available for treatment of acute and chronic alcoholism are either wholly inadequate or strained to the limit.

If the numbers of alcoholics and potential alcoholics constitute a public health problem that cannot be ignored, equally important are the many others in each community whose health and welfare are jeopardized by alcoholism—to begin with, those who are closest to, or dependent on, the problem drinker himself. If one assumes three persons per family, it becomes clear that in a large city such as Chicago, where there are over 290,000 alcoholics[3] (see Table 2), nearly a million lives could be immediately involved in this one illness. Whether or not excessive drinking actually breaks up the family (the divorce and separation rate of problem drinkers is significantly higher than that of the general population),[4] it inevitably undermines both the economic and social structure of the family. The cost of alcoholism in terms of emotional damage cannot, of course, be estimated, but its contribution to the problem of welfare and relief administration can: a 1954 survey showed 28 per cent of nonsupport cases in Chicago involved alcoholics.[5] About 20 million dollars a year is spent by voluntary agencies to care for the families of alcoholics, and roughly the same amount by public agencies.[6]

An important causative factor in *accidental injuries and*

fatalities, excessive drinking probably most endangers the community in the area of traffic safety. Alcohol is variously considered to be at least partly responsible for from 30 to 50 per cent[7] of the annual traffic accident toll, which in 1959, according to the National Safety Council, was 37,600 deaths and 2,870,000 injuries.[8] Not all who "drink and drive" are problem drinkers, of course. But the driver who drinks heavily plays a major role in the traffic death and injury problem, as is indicated by the results of four separate investigations shown in Table 13.

Table 13
The Role of Alcohol in Fatal Traffic Accidents[9]

Community	Years Covered	Driver Fatali- ties	% Drink- ing Drivers	% of Drivers with Blood Alcohol Levels		
				over 0.15	0.05- 0.15	0.01- 0.04
Westchester County (N.Y.)	1950- 1957	83*	73	49	20	4
Cleveland (Ohio)	1937- 1955	885	54	40	12	2
Maryland	1950- 1959	983	69	40	22	6
Middlesex County (N.J.)	1948- 1949	264	50	17	33	—

* Single-vehicle accidents, death within 4 hours.

Many physicians consider automobile accidents the nation's leading health problem and are taking the lead in getting legislation passed that will, among other things, curtail the number of alcoholic drivers on the road. Two laws are considered most urgent: (1) an implied consent-type law in every state that would give police the right to ask for a blood alcohol determination of drivers suspected of being under the influence of alcohol; (2) a lesser offense law that would reduce the prima facie level of intoxication from the present 0.15% to 0.10%.[10]

Alcohol contributes to other accidental deaths and injuries as well. In a recent study by Wilentz and Brady, who performed autopsies on 2,008 victims of violent death, ethyl alcohol was a contributing or responsible factor not only in 49 per cent of auto casualties, but also in 31 per cent of homicides, in 36 per cent of suicides, and in 39 per cent of deaths due to such accidents as burns, carbon monoxide poisoning, drownings, electrocutions, falls, and industrial accidents.

The two million alcoholics *in industry,* who represent 3 per cent of the working population, have a somewhat higher accident rate than that of other employees. It is suggested, however, that accidents probably play a lesser role in the heavy expense alcoholism creates for industry—about half a billion dollars yearly—than the alcoholic's absenteeism and reduced efficiency.[11]

In 1943, Jellinek estimated that employed alcoholics were absent an average of 22 days a year because of intoxication and its after-effects.[12] Later surveys confirm the fact that absenteeism among problem drinkers is considerably higher than the usual six to ten days of most employees. Percentages, however, vary from company to company and from job to job. In one study, high-status alcoholics, such as executives, engineers, and lawyers, often came to work despite heavy hangovers but then simply went through the motions of working; lower-status unskilled and semiskilled workers tended to absent themselves completely when feeling bad, or resorted to "partial absenteeism," leaving the job when the urge to drink became too strong.[13]

Although there is no exact way to measure the problem drinker's reduction in job efficiency, it seems reasonable to assume that the depressant effects of alcohol as well as the inevitable hangover, with its headache, fatigue, irritability, and tremor, must seriously interfere with coordination and concentration. In the early stages of alcoholism, the employee may try to improve his efficiency by drinking on the job just enough to control his growing restlessness. As his disorder worsens, however, his performance becomes increasingly inferior.

The costs to a particular company of problem-drinking employees may vary—with the amount invested in training, the damage created by prolonged work inefficiency, the expense involved in replacement if alcoholics are discharged or reach a stage where they can no longer work—but they are usually high. Many companies, therefore, have found it profitable either to set up rehabilitation programs of their own or to cooperate with medical and social agencies in the community by establishing adequate counseling and referral facilities. Because the problem drinker in industry tends to be an "early" or "middle-stage" alcoholic and still has relatively stable family, job and community relationships, he is more responsive to treatment than those alcoholics with more advanced physical and emotional abnormalities and "those who invest in his rehabilitation have some reason for optimism."[14]

Persons *arrested and held for drunkenness* are an even greater expense to the community; although rarely committing crimes serious enough to land them in federal or state prisons, they probably account for 70 per cent of the annual costs of maintaining county and local jails.[15] The tremendous cost of this "penal approach" to alcoholism can be judged by considering one city—Washington, D.C.—which spent $2,847.60 on June 30, 1953, to maintain the 1,017 alcoholics in jail for that day. Assuming June 30 to be an average day, Washington therefore spent about one million dollars in the year 1953 to maintain, without treatment, the alcoholic population of the city's correctional institutions. In addition to custodial expense, "drunk" arrests place an enormous burden on the various law enforcement agencies; three-quarters of all matters coming before the municipal court in Washington, D.C., in 1953 involved persons arrested for intoxication cases, with many offenders habitually serving five, six, and seven sentences a year.[16] While the percentage of alcoholics in the jail population is high, most have been sentenced for misdemeanors rather than for felonies, and *the contribution of excessive drinking to major crime* is probably often overestimated. Many criminals are heavy drinkers, of course. In a recent study of 2,325 male felons,[17] only 2 per cent were abstainers and, of the remaining 98 per cent, over half (51.6 per cent) had previously been arrested on drinking charges, almost 30 per cent felt alcohol was a problem in their lives, and about half claimed to have been drinking before committing the crime for which they had been sentenced. However, there are obviously many factors involved in the making of a criminal, and heavy drinking probably does most of its damage by heightening a criminal's courage and removing his inhibitions. In this area alone, it is dangerous enough—in the study cited, the crimes committed most often after or while drinking were homicide, assault, and auto theft.

NOTES

1. Landis, B.Y., *Quart. J. Stud. Alcohol,* 6:59, 1945.
2. Malzburg, B., *Cohort Studies of Mental Disease in New York State 1943-1949,* (New York: National Association for Mental Health, 1958).
3. Gelber, I., *Alcoholism in New York City* (New York: Department of Health, 1960), p. 12.
4. Baily, M.B., *Quart. J. Stud. Alcohol,* 22:81, 1961.
5. Harris, E.L., paper read at Veterans Administration Symposium on Alcoholism, Chicago, May 9, 1956.
6. Block, M. A., *Am. Assoc. Industr. Nurses J.,* 7:24 (Apr.) 1959.
7. Wilentz, W. C. and Brady, J. F., *Amer. Pract.,* 12:829, 1961.
8. National Safety Council, *Accident Facts* (Chicago: 1960).
9. Campbell, H. E., *J.A.M.A.,* 176:637, 1961.
10. Woodward, Fletcher D., *Virginia Med. Monthly,* 87:227, 1960.
11. Trice, H. M., *The Problem Drinker on the Job* (Ithaca, New York: New York State School of Industrial and Labor Relations, Cornell University, 1959).

12. Jellinek, E. M., in *Vital Speeches,* 13:252, 1947.
13. Trice, H. M., *ILR Res.* 4:10, 1958.
14. Trice, *op. cit.*
15. Landis, *loc. cit.*
16. Zappala, A., *Public Health Rep.,* 69:1187, 1954.
17. Division of Alcoholic Rehabilitation, *Criminal Offenders and Drinking Involvement* (Berkeley, California: Department of Public Health, 1960, publication no. 3.

10 Prognosis in Alcoholism

CURE OF A CHRONIC DISEASE

Do alcoholics ever get well? And if so, which among them stand the best chances? An answer is not possible without defining the term "recovery" in the context of alcoholism. Alcoholism is a chronic disease that runs an unusual variety of courses and shows marked tendency to recurrence.[1]

Cure, in the sense of a regained ability to drink socially, is rare; having passed the borderline into pathological drinking, the alcoholic usually must abstain totally. On the other hand, the arrestability of alcoholism—when measured in terms of total abstinence—appears to be now within reach of a gratifying number of patients.[2] Results vary greatly with the personality problems involved, the duration of the disease, the possibilities of controlling the patient's environment, and the psychiatric and medical treatments applied.[3]

Since the illness is almost certainly emotionally based,[4] the chances of arresting it depend to a considerable extent on the patient's degree of motivation toward change. All too often, for a positive motivation to develop something must "happen" to the alcoholic, perhaps the threatened loss of his family, his job, or his physical health. Sometimes, he may actually have to suffer these losses—reach what many alcoholics term "the low bottom"—before he will face the realities of his situation and determine to do something about it.[5] But in many cases motivation can be instilled; in the acute post-alcoholic episode, for instance, a maudlin and remorseful patient, susceptible to his physician's urgings, may be willing to begin treatment despite his original reservations. If the therapy administered can ease the difficult immediate post-alcoholic period and successfully break the cycle, then much unnecessary suffering is eliminated at this point and a tragedy may be averted.[5]

With so many factors to consider, it is not astonishing to note the widely divergent recovery rates, ranging in reports from a low of 3 per cent to a high of 80 per cent.[6,7] These, however, are extremes; mean recovery rates between 50 and 75 per cent seem to present sounder and more often observed averages of sobriety attained and maintained by new and comprehensive treatment methods.[8]

CONSULTATION AND ASSISTANCE

The increasing acceptance of alcoholism as a medical problem reflects not only a more enlightened attitude on the part of society but also—equally important—new modalities of therapy now available to the physician. Important discoveries in psychopharmacology make it feasible for him to manage some of the principal emotional and physical factors associated with the disorder. At the same time, a growing number of social, civic and religious agencies stand ready to supplement the individual physician's efforts.

The best known and most widely available of these resources is, of course, Alcoholics Anonymous, which has more

Table 16
Useful Prognostic Index of Alcoholism Clinic

A total rating of 0 or higher indicates a good prognosis; a negative total index score, a poor prognosis. Used in this manner, the index correctly identified 80 per cent of the successes and failures of a validation group of 60 cases.[9]

Criteria		Assigned weights
Marital status	Married:	½
	Separated or divorced:	-1
Economic resources	Good:	1
	Fair:	-½
	Poor:	-1
Usual occupation	Skilled, clerical, sales, prof'l:	1
	Unskilled:	-1
Arrest record	Under 5 arrests:	1
	20 or more arrests or prolonged incarceration:	-1
Motivation	Good:	1
	Fair:	-½
	Poor:	-1
Intellectual functioning	Superior or very superior:	1
	Below average or defective:	-1
Diagnosis	Obsessive-compulsive:	1
	Hysteria:	-½
	Schizophrenic, organic or sociopathic:	-1
Rorschach sign balance	1 or better:	1
	-2 or worse:	-1

than 7,000 local chapters; at least one exists in almost every sizable town. Though many problem drinkers cannot adjust to the "intense group life"[10] of the AA program, those who do attend meetings regularly and try to adhere to the "Twelve Steps" (which begin with the admission that the individual is powerless over alcohol and that his life has become unmanageable) appear to have a good chance of maintaining sobriety. For a number of alcoholics, the AA program fulfills such basic needs as those for status, for acceptance, for "structure" and for dependency.[11] Further, each new member is confronted immediately with proof of the group's effectiveness by meeting members who have achieved sobriety. Valuable as it is, Alcoholics Anonymous is not an organization of professionals, and considering it a complete form of therapy is dangerous. Rather, it should be "considered as an adjunct to and not a substitute for various forms of professional therapy."[12]

The relatives of the problem drinker, who frequently are the first to seek the family physician's help, may be referred to Al-Anon Family Groups—an organization allied to Alcoholics Anonymous. Here, too, members attend regular meetings in the community and discuss with other relatives of problem drinkers questions common to them all.

Relatives and friends might also be referred to one of the many Alcoholism Information Centers where they can obtain such pamphlets as "Alcoholic in the Family" and "The Alcoholic Spouse." These centers are affiliated with the National Council on Alcoholism (NCA), a voluntary agency with headquarters in New York City and councils in 61 cities, and serve as a clearinghouse of information on alcoholism. In addition to collecting and disseminating literature, they frequently assume leadership in providing the community with planned programs. They are a particularly useful source of information to the physician, since most of them search out and keep on file all the local treatment facilities for handling problem drinkers.

Other sources of information about local facilities are state and county medical societies, for many of them now have active subcommittees on alcoholism. And both the American Medical Association and the National Council on Alcoholism publish directories listing resources on alcoholism in the various states.

According to the NCA's most recent directory, over 160 communities now have outpatient alcoholism clinics and counseling services, many of them state or county-supported. The typical outpatient clinic offers a "multipronged, multidisciplined" approach to alcoholism with a staff consisting of psychiatrists, internists, clinical psychologists, public health nurses, and social workers. The patient, therefore, frequently receives a combination of medical, psychiatric, and social care at these institutions.[13] In addition to clinics supported by hospitals or public health departments, private businesses have organized and now support a growing number of treatment centers. Some companies operate rehabilitation programs designed to recognize and treat their own alcoholic employees. Other firms jointly underwrite, or support, treatment centers, such as the Chicago Committee on Alcoholism (supported by 300 companies) and the Clinic for Alcoholism at the NYU-Bellevue Medical Center, that function as a service for the entire community as well as for the employees of the individual companies.[14] A number of private clinics specialize in the rehabilitation of alcoholics and might be the answer when cost is not a consideration.

Along with agencies specializing in the problem of alcoholism, more and more of the general agencies—mental health clinics, family care agencies, general hospitals, vocational rehabilitation services, and others—are also beginning to realize that they can serve alcoholics effectively.[15] Their realization is encouraging, because such agencies, chosen by the physician to supplement his own medical or psychiatric therapy, can play an important role in the rehabilitation of the problem drinker.

NOTES

1. Gold, H., et. al., (eds.), Cornell Conferences on Therapy (New York: Macmillan, 1949), vol. 3, pp. 253 ff.
2. Pfeffer, A. Z., Alcoholism (New York: Grune, 1958), p. 6.
3. Gold, op. cit.
4. Shield, J. A., Virginia Med. Monthly 88.102, 1961.
5. Feldman, D. J. and Zucker, H. D., J.A.M.A. 153:895, 1953.
6. Foster, M. W., Ment. Hosp., 10:35, 1959.
7. Shephard, E. A., J. Florida Med. Assoc., 45:906, 1959.
8. Fox, R., New York J. Med., 58:1540, 1958.
9. Mindlin, D. F., Quart. J. Stud. Alcohol, 20:604, 1959.
10. Golin, M., J.A.M.A., 167:1496, 1958.

11. Van Suetendael, P. T., *Milit. Med.*, 124:851, 1959.
12. Willard, W. R. and Straus, R., *New York Med. J.*, 58:2256, 1958.
13. Zappala, A. and Ketcham, F. S., *Public Health Rep.*, 69:1187, 1954.
14. Mindlin, *loc. cit.*
15. Brightman, I. J., *ibid.*, 75:775, 1960.

11 The Problem of Prevention

In alcoholism, an ounce of prevention is indeed worth a good deal more than its weight in cure. On the surface, the prevention of alcoholism depends upon a single premise: one attempts to keep the "host" away from the "causative agent." Failing that, one tries to keep the "causative agent" away from the "host." To these ends countless maneuvers have been attempted, among them "restrictive legislation, authoritarian fiat, appeals to intelligence or to spiritual motive, increased retail prices for various beverages, arrests and sentences for drunkenness, revocation of license for driving under the influence, increased taxation on the beverage industry."[1] But unfortunately, the net result of these acts of prevention, even when applied with full legal force and fury, has so far been rather negligible.

PERSUASION, THE FIRST WEAPON

Earlier ages also found the task of keeping drinker and alcohol apart a monumental one. Until a comparatively short time ago, persuasion—not the most potent of weapons—was almost the only one available in the war against excessive drinking. About 3000 years ago, an emotional Egyptian wrote what may have been the first temperance tract. "Take not upon thyself to drink a jug of beer," he pleaded in a work called *Wisdom of Ani,* because if you do, "thou speakest, and an unintelligible utterance issueth from thy mouth. If thou fallest down and thy limbs break, there is none to hold out a hand to thee. Thy companions in drink stand up and say: 'Away with this sot.' If there then cometh one to seek thee in order to question thee, thou art found lying on the ground, and thou art like a little child."[2]

Whether this depressing portrait had much effect on Egyptian problem drinkers is not known. But in the *Shu Ching,* written about 650 B.C., the Chinese advice to potential alcohol misusers starts out by admitting, "Men will not do without *kiu* [a form of beer]. To prohibit it and secure total abstinence from it is beyond the power even of sages. Here, therefore, we have warnings on the abuse of it." The warnings, recommending moderation, are fairly well summed up by the often quoted Japanese proverb: "At the first cup, man drinks wine. At the second cup, wine drinks wine. At the third cup, wine drinks man."[3]

The Book of Proverbs, while it strongly denounces the misuse of alcohol, apparently does not frown upon moderation. "Give strong drink unto him that is ready to perish," it counsels "and wine unto those that be of heavy hearts. Let him drink, and forget his poverty, and remember his misery no more."

THE RISE AND FALL OF PROHIBITION

If the concept of total abstinence was almost entirely absent in earlier civilizations, it was equally foreign to the colonists who first came to America from England.

For the colonists, as for their ancestors, alcohol had religious, medical, dietary, and recreational significance. It also had commercial significance: the manufacture of rum became for a long time New England's largest industry. In various parts of the new country, converting corn and other grains into whiskey soon proved to be the most profitable way of transporting "crops" to market.

The increasing popularity of distilled spirits was one of the factors that led to the strong "anti-drinking" movement in the United States. Before 1700—when drinking was largely confined to the home, and beer and wine were the favored drinks —warnings and mild punishment were generally enough to cope with occasional over-indulgence. But in the next century or so, drinking patterns changed.[4] Taverns appeared in every town, "hard" liquor was soon the common choice, and drunkenness became a problem to be reckoned with.

By the nineteenth century, many physicians had joined the growing temperance movement. Previously, alcohol had been widely considered to have medicinal virtues, if nothing else. But by the 1830's—following the lead of the famous Dr. Benjamin Rush—medical men were agreeing that alcohol actually served no useful purpose at all; it had no value as a medicine and, moreover, it did not, as was commonly believed, increase the working efficiency of farmers and laborers.

Clergymen too were developing new theories about the use of alcohol. A good many, re-examining the Bible's apparent sanction of moderate drinking, came to a radical new conclusion. When the Bible appeared to sanction the use of wine, they held, it was referring to *unfermented* grape use; when it condemned the use of wine, it was, however, referring to the *fermented* variety.

Thus, the way was clear to advocate total abstinence. Between 1840 and 1860 a number of temperance groups formed, such as the Sons of Temperance and the Independent Order of Good Templars, whose philosophy was no longer opposition to the more than occasional use of "hard" liquor, but was now opposition to the use of alcoholic beverages of any kind and at any time.[5]

To achieve the new goal of total abstinence, legal enforcement seemed to be essential. The strong influence of the Templars made the question of prohibition suddenly an important nationwide political issue and in 1872 the National Prohibition Party first appeared on the ticket with their platform: "Complete Suppression of the Trade in Intoxicating Liquors."

Two years later, the Women's Christian Temperance Union was formed to aid in the fight for total abstinence, declaring its purpose to be "to educate the young; to form a better public sentiment; to reform so far as possible, by religious, ethical and scientific means, the drinking classes; to seek the transforming power of divine grace for ourselves and for all for whom we work." The most influential and highly organized temperance group of all, the Anti-Saloon League, came into being in 1895. Its members pledged, through "Education, Legislation and Law Enforcement," to eliminate drinking in the United States.[6]

Conditions during the first two decades of the twentieth century were ideal for the temperance groups' purpose. A rapid increase in population, due chiefly to stepped-up immigration, and growing industrialization had led to dramatic and often unfavorable changes in modes of urban living. For practical and humanitarian reasons, the period 1900 to 1919 had to be one of sweeping social reforms. And since for many humanitarians the problems of the congested cities' new inhabitants could be blamed on alcohol, the desire to "do something for the working classes" reinforced the drive to eliminate their alcohol.

By 1919, the concept of prohibition had been publicized for over half a century and had been adopted in various parts of the country. But "local option" clearly had many flaws— temperance leaders were well aware that those who wanted liquor could travel out of their communities to get it. Only nationwide prohibition, they felt, had any chance of stopping the potential alcoholic. In this year, "humanitarian zeal combined with a spiritul motive"[7] led to the passage of the 18th Amendment, which prohibited the manufacture and sale of distilled intoxicating liquors.

In October of 1919, Congress passed the Volstead Act, which provided the machinery for administering and enforcing the 18th Amendment. However, almost from the very start, indifference and even resistance to the enforcement of the law by both officials and private citizens served to render it ineffective. The one essential ingredient for the successful enforcement of a prohibition law was lacking—popular support. In 1933, it was generally acknowledged that the 18th Amendment had failed and the law was repealed. There was, however, no reason for rejoicing, as one observer noted. "If prohibition laws have not solved the liquor problem, neither has the absence of prohibition laws. The records of the centuries give wets and drys little cause for arrogance and much cause for humility."[8]

OTHER LEGAL APPROACHES TO ALCOHOLISM CONTROLS

After 1933, state legislatures settled down to devising liquor control systems that would, as much as possible, protect the individual from his own weakness. A great variety of legislation has since been passed to control all stages of production, distribution, and sale of alcoholic beverages.

Though the laws vary among the different states, in general, most states have adopted either a monopoly plan—by which a board or commission purchases liquor and sells it through official stores—or a license system under which a state commission grants licenses to private citizens for the sale of alcoholic beverages. In either system, liquor boards and commissions prohibit sales to minors and intoxicated persons, and make a determined effort to prevent disreputable persons from becoming associated with the liquor industry.

Aside from these areas of agreement, liquor laws differ widely from community to community on such matters as zoning, sanitation, labeling, advertising, shipping, service of food with drinks, permits for purchases and the like.[9] Since local option laws are in effect in the majority of the states, many cities and towns in the country are legally "dry." And perhaps the favorite legal measure of all, taxation of the liquor industry, has the virtue of being a reasonably "painless" way of raising taxes whether or not it deters liquor purchases.

Can strong legislative measures control or at least retard the development of alcoholism? Probably not. Most observers feel that legal controls affect the social drinker much more than they do the alcoholic.[10]

The heavy drinker can—and should—be controlled to some extent by such measures as "drunk driving" laws, particularly when they are reinforced by social pressures and well thought out educational programs. But the alcoholic is usually immune to both social and legal pressure.

PREVENTION OF PROGRESSION

Since preventing the onset of alcoholism appears, at the present time, to be beyond our powers, *secondary* prevention —early intervention in excessive and pathological drinking in order to prevent the major consequences of alcoholism[11]—

takes on paramount importance. Here, at least, the essential tools already exist. By now, almost all physicians, clergymen, social workers, and public health personnel are aware of the warning signs of alcoholism, and diagnosis in the earlier stages is possible.

According to most observers, no individual is a better "secondary preventer" than the family physician. Patients and their families tend to come to him first for help with a drinking problem (though the problem may often be disguised). In addition, changes in drinking habits—usually the first sign of potential trouble—can often be detected during a careful medical history. For this reason, it has been suggested that all physicians include questions about alcohol intake in the course of routine case-taking.[12] When a drinking problem appears to be more than just a possibility, a number of physicians now include a questionnaire, such as the one developed by the late Robert V. Seliger (Johns Hopkins University Medical School)[13] to determine how serious the problem may be (see below). In each question this test deals with a sign that has appeared so consistently in the early records of abnormal drinking that there can be no doubt that it is a danger signal. Aside from the patient himself, it is suggested that the questions be also answered by the patient's mate, or a friend.

1. Do you require a drink the next morning?
2. Do you prefer to drink alone?
3. Do you lose time from work due to drinking?
4. Is your drinking harming your family in any way?
5. Do you need a drink at a definite time daily?
6. Do you get the inner shakes unless you continue drinking?
7. Has drinking made you irritable?
8. Does it make you careless of your family's welfare?

9. Have you become jealous of your husband or wife since drinking?

10. Has drinking changed your personality?

11. Does it cause you body complaints?

12. Does it make you restless?

13. Does it cause you to have difficulty in sleeping?

14. Has it made you more impulsive?

15. Have you less self-control since drinking?

16. Has your initiative decreased?

17. Has your ambition decreased?

18. Do you lack perseverance in pursuing a goal since drinking?

19. Do you drink to obtain social ease? (In shy, timid, self-conscious individuals.)

20. Do you drink for self-encouragement? (In persons with feelings of inferiority.)

21. To relieve marked feelings of inadequacy?

22. Has your sexual potency suffered since drinking?

23. Do you show marked dislikes and hatreds?

24. Has your jealousy, in general, increased?

25. Do you show marked moodiness as a result of drinking?

26. Has your efficiency decreased?

27. Has your drinking made you more sensitive?

28. Are you harder to get along with?

29. Do you turn to an inferior environment while drinking?

30. Is drinking endangering your health?

31. Is it affecting your peace of mind?

32. Is it making your home life unhappy?

33. Is it jeopardizing your business?

34. Is it clouding your reputation?

35. Is drinking disturbing the harmony of your life?

In the earlier stages of alcoholism, the personal physician can do much to prevent the patient from deteriorating into the chronic phase. "It is important," suggests Brightman, "to make a complete diagnosis of the patient's condition, including a determination of whether addiction is present, the rapidity with which the alcoholic pattern is changing, the relationship of the drinking to underlying mental and physical disorders and the importance of various social or environmental factors." The physician's sympathy and understanding are also important concomitants of treatment.

As far as medical treatment itself is concerned, the past few years have seen the development of drugs and techniques which have led to greatly increased effectiveness in the management of the alcoholic. Psychopharmaceutical medication, now available to control the problem drinker's anxiety and tension, often reduces the need for alcohol's tension-reducing properties and helps make the patient more accessible to psychological counseling. Drugs such as disulfiram—which sensitizes the individual to alcohol so that ingestion of even a small amount results in illness—are helpful with certain types of patients. All in all, "while alcoholism is still a very difficult disease to treat and requires much patience and detailed planning on the part of the physician, there is now a greater possibility of obtaining gratifying results than existed ten or fifteen years ago."[14]

NOTES

1. R. G. McCarthy and E. M. Douglass, in R. G. McCarthy (ed.), *Drinking and Intoxication* (Glencoe, Ill.: The Free Press, 1959).
2. B. Roueche, *Neutral Spirit: A Portrait of Alcohol* (Toronto: Little, Brown & Co., 1960).
3. *Ibid.*
4. R. Straus and S. D. Bacon, *Drinking in College* (New Haven: Yale University Press, 1953).
5. McCarthy and Douglass, *op. cit.*
6. *Ibid.*
7. *Ibid.*
8. A. Coates, *Popular Government*, 4:1, 1937.
9. Straus and Bacon, *op. cit.*

10. M. E. Chafetz and H. W. Demone, Jr., Alcoholism and Society (New York: Oxford University Press, 1962).

11. *Ibid.*

12. I. J. Brightman, in H. E. Hilleboe and G. W. Larimore (eds.), *Preventive Medicine* (Philadelphia: W. B. Saunders Co., 1959).

13. R. V. Seliger, V. Cranford, and H. S. Goodwin, *J. Clin. Psychopath.*, 6:145, 1944.

14. Brightman, *loc. cit.*

12 Do's and Don't's for the Family

ATTITUDES AND "HOME TREATMENT"

Alcoholism is frequently referred to as a "family illness," because within the confines of the family alcoholism commonly causes major difficulties and emotional harm. In the treatment of the problem drinker, family attitudes present obstacles which must be removed before recovery can begin. They often intensify the alcoholic's need to escape into drink and to strengthen his distorted view of himself and others.[1,2]

By the time the problem drinker is seen by the physician, the family has often done more harm than good with "home treatment" methods of lecturing, weeping, pleading and various other emotional appeals. As a result, the physician will often decide to include the wife (or husband), as well as other family members, within the scope of his therapeutic efforts in an attempt to restore their psychological balance and to help them develop a realistic insight into the existing problem as an illness.

When advising family members on how to deal with their alcoholic, the following rules[3-11] have been found valuable.

Do's	*Don't's*
1. Learn the facts about alcoholism. A variety of authoritative booklets for the layman are available through the A.M.A., Chicago; the National Council on Alcoholism, New York; and other organizations. Attend meetings of AA and Al-Anon Family Groups with an "open mind" to learn and benefit from the experience of others.	1. Don't preach, nag, lecture and assume a "holier-than-thou" attitude; which the alcoholic's characteristic low tolerance of frustration, such will probably cause him to escape more and more into alcoholism.
2. Develop an attitude, reflecting insight, to match the facts that you have learned about alcoholism and the alcoholic.	2. Never use emotional appeals such as "If you loved me": they only tend to increase feelings of guilt and the compulsive need to drink.
3. Test your attitude by taking honest personal inventory of yourself: "Are you convinced that alcoholism really is a disease?" "Is your approach to the alcoholic one of love, indifference, or rejection?"	3. Be sure not to make threats you don't intend to carry out or will not be able to follow through.
4. Discuss the situation with a trusted layman—a clergyman or a social worker—or a person who has experienced some phase of alcoholism, either as an alcoholic or as a family member.	4. Do not look upon your alcoholic as a moral weakling or completely take over his responsibilities, leaving him with no sense of importance or value.
5. Take it as a matter of course	5. Don't shelter your alcoholic

when your alcoholic stops drinking, either as a result of self-help or of formal treatment; observe complete alcohol abstinence yourself, because drinking on the part of the nonalcoholic mate is unconsciously resented by the alcoholic and may make him resume drinking.

6. Establish and maintain a healthy atmosphere in the home, with a sympathetic place in the family circle for the alcoholic member.

7. Encourage new interests and participate whenever possible in recreational or occupational activities enjoyed by your alcoholic; encourage him to see old friends.

8. Be patient and live one day at a time: alcoholism takes a long time to develop; recovery doesn't happen overnight. Accept setbacks and relapses with equanimity. Keep on trying.

9. Approach the alcoholic about his drinking problem only when he is sober—for ex-

from situations where alcohol is present: don't hide bottles or pour liquor down the sink. Such acts only impel him to establish a secret supply hidden from you and certainly do not aid him in successfully facing the everyday temptation of drinking in our society.

6. Never extract promises or place your alcoholic in a position where he or she must be deceitful. Pledges readily given and broken intensify the alcoholic's guilt feelings and loss of self-respect.

7. Be sure not to argue or put pressure on the alcoholic when he is drinking or intoxicated —the response is usually one of negativism and even violence. Never resort to physical violence or punishment.

8. Never be overconfident or expect a recovery that is either immediate or complete.

9. Don't cover up or make excuses for the alcoholic.

ample, shortly after a bout, when hangover, depression, and remorse are present.

10. Discreetly place injurious objects out of sight, and attempt to withhold car keys when your alcoholic becomes intoxicated.

10. Try not to be a martyr, to feel ashamed or at fault. These attitudes will only serve to destroy objectivity and usually are sensed by the already remorseful, suspicious alcoholic.

11. Explain the nature of alcoholism as an illness to children in the family; try to spare their seeing the alcholic parent in an extremely intoxicated state.

11. Avoid making an issue over, or standing in judgment of, the method of recovery selected by your alcoholic.

12. Advise local bartenders and police, whenever possible, about your alcoholic's condition to help prevent community incidents and embarrassments.

12. Never use the children as tools or turn them against the alcoholic in an attempt to cope with your problems.

MENTAL CHANGES IN ALCOHOLISM

Although the psychopathology in alcoholism varies with the individual, the chronic alcoholic does tend to develop along a particular "character matrix."[14] Certain pre-existing mental traits, present before the alcoholic actually takes to drinking, frequently become increasingly pronounced as excessive amounts of alcohol are taken. For some reason, the alcoholic cannot and does not use the neurotic traits of the relatively well-adjusted or the overt symptoms of the psychoneurotic to deal with his anxiety in times of stress. Rather, he finds his solution in alcohol.[15]

Table 17 exhibits some of the mental and personality changes frequently encountered in the alcoholic patient.

Table 17
Common Mental and Personality Changes in the Alcoholic[16-20]

Traits	Their Expression
1. Egocentricity	Self-centered view of his problems—extreme narcissism, primary concern with self and need to drink; in later stages, promises or does anything to maintain his supply of alcohol.
2. Paranoid ideas	Accusations of marital infidelity by alcoholic mate, offers of help and expressions of concern misinterpreted as "picking on him."
3. Ambivalence of feelings	Expressions of love as well as of annoyance and hostility toward mate, family members and friends; alternating attitudes whereby he seeks, and then rejects, treatment and/or help.
4. Inconsistency	Excessive deviations in behavior, often impulsive in nature; undependable at home, at work and in other situations, all because of drinking which must be done; extraordinary fears.
5. Lack of insight	Rationalizations and tendency to blame others and his environment for his compulsive need to drink, creation of myth that he can control his drinking, attitude of indifference to cover up feelings of shame and degradation.
6. Arrogance and defiance	Grandiosity of thought and of discourse, masking feelings of inferiority and inadequacy; aggressive acting out of resentments and hostility against family, friends, and others, often leading to fights; sadistic traits.
7. Moods of depression	Deep feelings of guilt, remorse, and self-accusation after a bout, general avoidance of discussion or admission of drinking, occasional outbursts of self-disgust and desire to stop, masochistic inclinations.

NOTES

1. Conn, H. F., Current Therapy (Philadelphia: Saunders, 1959), pp. 489-90.
2. The National Council on Alcoholism, Inc., "Alcoholic in the Family; Alcoholism—Hidden Malady and Anonymous Recovery; Don't Tell Me I'm Not an Alcoholic; Do's and Don't's for the Wives of Alcoholics; How to Know an Alcoholic; The Alcoholic Spouse; The Ego Factors in Surrender in Alcoholism; Alcoholism—Disease or Disgrace?; Conversion as a Psychological Phenomenon; Family Relationships Contributing to Alcoholism (New York: National Council).

3. Fox, R., paper read at Annual Meeting, National Council on Alcoholism, Inc., Salt Lake City, 1959.
4. Fox, R. and Lyon, P., *Alcoholism* (New York: Random House, 1955), pp. 70ff.
5. Jellinek, E. M., *The Disease Concept of Alcoholism* (New Haven: Hillhouse, 1960), pp. 33ff.
6. Kant, F., *The Treatment of the Alcoholic* (Springfield, Ill.: Thomas, 1954), pp. 12-16, 21ff.
7. Mann, M., *Primer on Alcoholism* (New York: Rinehart, 1950), *passim*.
8. Miller, M., *Med. Times,* 89:811, 1961.
9. Pfeffer, A. Z., *Alcoholism* (New York: Grune, 1958), pp. 29-50.
10. The National Council on Alcoholism, Inc. See Footnote 2.
11. Zwerling, I. and Rosenbaum, M., *American Handbook of Psychiatry* (New York: Basic Books, 1959), vol. 1, pp. 623-44.
12. Bell, R. G., *Canad. Med. Assoc. J.,* 83:1348, 1960.
13. Noyes, A. P., *Modern Clinical Psychiatry* (Philadelphia: Saunders, ed. 4, 1953), pp. 183-203.
14. Zwerling and Rosenbaum, *loc. cit.*
15. Noyes, *loc. cit.*
16. Lemert, E. M., *Quart. J. Stud. Alcohol,* 21:679, 1960.
17. McCarthy, R. G., *Amer. J. Nurs.,* 59:203, 1959.
18. Mann, *op. cit.*
19. Al-Anon, *You and the Alcoholic; Alcoholism, the Family Disease* (pamphlets) (New York: The Al-Anon Family Groups Headquarters, Inc.).
20. The National Council on Alcoholism, Inc. See Footnote 2.

13 Drinking, an International Problem

Since alcoholic beverages are freely available in most countries (and at least procurable in others), the alcoholic obviously may be encountered almost anywhere in the world. Yet he apparently is seen much more frequently in some countries than in others. Moreover, the public's attitude toward his condition, the medical treatment of it, and, in some cases, the basic underlying causes for its onset also may differ from one country to the next.

Even the term "alcoholism" itself may have varied meanings to foreign experts on the subject, and Jellinek suggests that the meaning of the word be extended beyond the conception which is current in America and some Anglo-Saxon countries. Pointing out that there is not just one form of alcoholism but several, Jellinek has described the most common "species" of alcoholism as:[1]

(a) Alpha Alcoholism, a purely psychological dependence upon alcohol for relief of bodily or emotional pain and with no signs of progression;

(b) Beta Alcoholism, in which the complications of alcoholism, such as gastritis, may occur simply because of heavy social drinking and with no signs of physical or psychological dependence;

(c) Gamma Alcoholism, in which both psychological and physical dependence are observed, the physical dependence being characterized by "loss of control";

(d) Delta Alcoholism, in which both psychological and physical dependence are observed, but in which physical dependence is characterized by an "inability to abstain" from alcohol rather than by a "loss of control".

Gamma Alcoholism is, of course, the species that predominates in the United States, and the tendency may be to consider it the only form of alcoholism. But in many countries, more serious problems may arise from one of the other types.

THE "INVETERATE DRINKER"—NEVER DRUNK, NEVER SOBER

Delta Alcoholism, rather than Gamma, is apparently the one that predominates in France and in several other wine-drinking countries such as Chile and Portugal. In these countries, a fairly steady morning-to-evening drinking pattern is common, and there is general social acceptance of large individual consumption. For instance, in a French survey carried out in 1953, answers by men to the question of what amount of wine a working man could drink every day "without any inconvenience" averaged 1.8 liters (slightly under two quarts).[2]

And a hard-drinking French citizen, particularly one who works in the wine-growing area, often drinks as much as three liters of wine a day, starting with a six-oz. glass of wine with breakfast and continuing at regular intervals throughout the day. The blood alcohol of such a man may range from a low of .02 per cent to about .12 per cent, rarely high enough to cause visible symptoms of intoxication in an experienced drinker.

Apparent consumption of alcohol* in certain countries of the population aged 15 years and over (last available year in each country).

Country	Year	Liters per capita
France	1955	25.72
Italy	1960	13.26
Switzerland	1950-55	10.85
Australia	1960-61	9.66
New Zealand	1960	9.03
Germany (West)	1960	8.84
Belgium	1960	8.48
U.S.A.	1962	7.99
Canada	1961	7.23
Hungary	1954	7.00
Peru	1957	6.55
United Kingdom	1960	6.16
Poland	1959	5.58
Denmark	1959	5.57
Sweden	1959	4.98
Germany (East)	1960	4.60
Ireland	1959	4.15
Israel	1959	3.68
Norway	1960	3.45
Finland	1960	3.33
Netherlands	1958	3.19

* As contained in distilled spirits, wine and beer.

Notes: Calculations for this table are based on the best available information from each country. It should be noted that they are "apparent" rather than actual, since they are derived from such available information as the amount of tax-paid wine delivered to distributors, and other indirect data. Only countries from which adequate statistics not more than 10 years old are available have been included in this tabulation.

Comparisons between countries are of dubious legitimacy when the time is not the same. Also of dubious validity is the use of the same population base (whether total, age 15 and over, or any other) for all countries, since the true proportion of drinkers is different in various countries. Only the per capita consumption of actual drinkers would give the most satisfactory comparison.

From: V. Efron and M. Keller, *Selected Statistical Tables on the Consumption of Alcohol, 1850-1962, and on Alcoholism, 1930-1960* (New Brunswick, N.J.; Rutgers Center of Alcohol Studies, 1963), p. 10.

Thus, many "inveterate drinkers" may be considered addicted to alcohol, yet they may go on indefinitely—never really drunk and never completely sober. Unlike the Gamma alcoholic, they usually show no loss of control over their drinking, have no compulsion to drink themselves into a stupor. However, since they often are unable to abstain from alcohol for even a day, they cannot—like so many of the alcoholics seen in the United States—"go on the wagon."

The causes of "inveterate drinking" appear, on the whole, more social and economic then psychiatric. The abundance and easy availability of wine and other alcoholic beverages encourages heavy drinking. (In Portugal, for instance, a pound of meat costs eleven escudos—and a quart of wine only two escudos.[3] Both the importance of wine-growing to the economy of the country and pride in the national product tend to bring about social approval of heavy individual consumption.

But socio-economic factors are hardly the whole answer. France's next-door neighbor is another large wine-growing country, Italy. Here, too, a sizable proportion of the population not only earn their living through the production and sale of wine but also consume a good deal of their product as well. Yet, according to available statistics, the rate of alcoholism in Italy is about five times lower than in France.

This may result from a different attitude toward drinking and drunkenness.[4] The Italian tends to accept the use of alcohol as a food to be taken in moderation and with meals. Though he may drink as much as a liter of wine a day, he probably will drink only with his noon and evening meal. Moreover, there is no social pressure to drink in Italy. Unlike the Frenchman, who often considers heavy drinking a proof of manhood,[5] the Italian will accept the abstainer's refusal without comment. Even more important, in Italy there is definite disapproval of more than moderate drinking, and also severe and consistent social sanctions against intoxication which are lacking in France.

Concerned about the number of "inveterate drinkers" in France, both the government and private citizens are striving to remedy the situation. The Council on Alcoholism and such voluntary agencies as Comité National de Défense Contre l'Alcoolisme concentrate primarily on preventive education, as well as the collection and dissemination of data on alcoholism.

The Russians, traditionally a hard-drinking people, have a capacity for vodka that many Western visitors find truly awe-inspiring. During the days of the Tsars, at any rate, one Russian writer described conditions in this way:

> And through the village there sounded the desperate howl of the wife: "The man drinks." And there rose up a tremendous, monstrous drinking seen nowhere else on God's earth, and it moved all across the Russian land, provoking drunkenness in all—in some, quiet, broken, sad; in others, wild and spirited. The *Kabaks* [taverns] caused drunkenness, drunkenness caused *zapoi* [the drinking without letting up, alcoholism], and for *zapoi* treatment was needed.[6]

According to the present Russian government, however, *zapoi* is no longer the serious problem it was in pre-revolutionary days, when about a third of all beds in mental hospitals were occupied by alcoholics. Professor Rapoport, speaking at the Moscow Ministry of Health, reported that, by 1953, only about 2 per cent of these beds were filled by alcoholics. Since 1950, about 5 or 6 persons per 10,000 of population have been applying for treatment of alcoholism each year.[7]

Treatment for the majority of alcoholics is given mostly in dispensaries; and methods include psychotherapy, individual and group hypnosis, various drugs, occupational therapy, and aversion treatment.[8] (The Russian's psychotherapy, however, is usually different from that of the Western world and appears to be closer to office counseling or "Dutch uncle" talks. Prof. Rapoport believes that this man-to-man talk is the best tool in dealing with alcoholics.)

On the whole, these methods of treatment are not unlike those in America. There appears to be more stress, though, on various forms of conditioned-reflex therapy, not too surprising in view of the fact that such methods are based on the classical conditioning studies of Pavlov. The Russians, in fact, were the first to issue a scientific report on the value of using this technique in the treatment of alcoholism.

In conditioned-reflex therapy—employed in this country, as well—the physician generally gives the alcoholic patient a short-acting emetic drug, such as apomorphine, waits five or ten minutes until the patient begins reacting to the drug, then lets him drink his favorite alcoholic beverage. Donald Hammersley describes a typical session:

As a strong wave of nausea developed, and before actual vomiting began, the patient was given one and one-half oz. of whiskey and told to swallow it. . . . If the administration of whiskey was properly timed, emesis occurred in less than thirty seconds after ingestion of whiskey.[9]

Following several highly unpleasant treatments of this nature, the patient, understandably enough, is conditioned to become nauseated at the sight of alcohol, to vomit at the first few mouthfuls. There are flaws in the system, of course: the strong resistance of many alcoholics to the whole procedure, the need for almost continuous medical supervision, and the gradual "deconditioning" of the alcoholic in the weeks following cessation of treatment.

A somewhat less painful version of this method is hypnotherapy, also popular in the Soviet Union. During hypnosis, reports Prof. I. Strelchuk,[10] the patient is exposed to the odor of an alcoholic beverage and given some to drink. At the same time, he is told that he not only has lost his desire for alcohol, but that even the odor or taste of it will, in the future, be highly unpleasant, will provoke nausea, severe headache, and dizziness. Such hypnotic suggestions, repeated every two or three days, eventually lead to a stable dislike for alcohol which may, in the majority of patients, last from four to six months. In patients with what Prof. Strelchuk calls a "pseudo withdrawal syndrome" characterized by an irritable-depressed psychic mood and an intense desire for alcohol, prolonged sleep therapy has proved quite effective. The patient is kept asleep, by a combination of hypnosis and hypnotic drugs, for 18 to 22 hours out of every 24 and is fed intravenously. When he awakes, five to ten days later, the pseudo withdrawal syndrome presumably has had a chance to wear itself out.

While the Soviet medical men specializing in alcoholism hold views concerning causes and treatment similar to those of our own specialists, the general Soviet physician and psychiatrist, according to Dr. Morris Chafetz[11] who studied the problem firsthand in Iron-Curtain countries, considers the alcoholic patient a delinquent and avoids treating him unless a medical complication is present. This attitude, Dr. Chafetz points out, is not uncommon in the United States. He concludes that, on the whole, "the Soviet attitude toward the alcoholic patient tends to be moralistic and punitive, as in the United States."

A "TOTAL APPROACH" TO ALCOHOLISM

Czechoslovakia is one of the few Iron Curtain countries in which alcoholism statistics can be obtained. These suggest that alcoholics make up roughly 2 per cent of the population (compared to about 3 per cent of the population in the United States.) According to Dr. Chafetz,[12] the Czechs, although they have fewer personnel than we have, in some cases have better facilities for dealing with the alcoholic. In addition, they have various treatment programs worthy of our study.

One innovation is the anti-alcoholic station to which intoxicated persons are brought by the police for "drying-out service." These stations, staffed principally by male nurses and by psychiatrists specializing in the treatment of alcoholism, not only provide medical treatment for acute alcoholic states but also serve as alcoholic detection centers. Upon discharge from the station, the patient's name is give to the district alcoholic center, and he must report to this center for a lecture on alcoholism. In addition, a district doctor is sent to call upon him to determine whether he is or is not an alcoholic. If the medical verdict is yes—or if the individual is seen at an anti-alcoholic station a second time—a psychiatrist is called in and long-term treatment is initiated.

Treatment of chronic alcoholism is usually conducted at an anti-alcoholic clinic and consists of individual and group therapy (often for the patient's mate as well) and disulfiram treatment. If these measures prove ineffective, the alcoholic is institutionalized for more intensive treatment. For instance, at the Apolinar (the main center for anti-alcoholic activities in Prague), an example of the Czech's "total approach" can be seen. The program stresses physical and mental rehabilitation and, in the words of a socialist-oriented physician, "is concerned to attract the attention of the patient from his own narrow, individual interests to the interests of a small community (roommates, family), a larger community (all patients in the department, people in the work place) and the whole community (society)."[13]

The three-month program includes psychotherapy, work treatment, and educational activities. One interesting idea is that of giving long-term abstainers particular recognition, encouraging them to help other alcoholics, even allowing them to work in alcoholism clinics as part of the clinic personnel. Abstainers who are actors and artists come to perform before alcoholic patients, thus helping in the "identification process," which is considered by the Czechs highly useful in helping the alcoholic maintain and create new self-respect.

NOTES

1. E. M. Jellinek, *The Disease Concept of Alcoholism* (New Haven: Hillhouse Press, 1960).
2. H. Bastide, *Population*, 9:13, 1954.
3. Jellinek, *op. cit.*
4. *Ibid.*
5. R. Sadoun and G. Lolli, *Quart. J. Stud. Alcohol*, 23:449, 1962.
6. V. Efron, *Quart. J. Stud. Alcohol*, 16:484, 1955.
7. *Scope Weekly*, 2:(2), 10, 1957.
8. V. Efron, *Quart. J. Stud. Alcohol*, 19:668, 1958.
9. D. W. Hammersley, in R. S. Wallerstein (ed.), *Hospital Treatment of Alcoholism* (New York: Basic Books, Inc., 1957).
10. *Medical Tribune*, 3:(14), 2, 1962.
11. M. E. Chafetz, *New England J. Med.*, 265:68, 1961.
12. *Ibid.*
13. *Ibid.*

Part II
Alcoholism
in Industry

14 The Problem Drinker

Until a few years ago business managers were likely to deny having any difficulty with employees who had a drinking problem. They generally maintained that if they discovered such persons in their organizations they fired them—after a few "last chances." But this attitude toward the alcoholic employee has changed. First a cautious inquisitiveness about the employee with a drinking problem developed among management, personnel executives, and union officials. More recently, instead of regarding such employees as moral degenerates, weak-willed and deserving of discipline or discharge, management has shown an inclination to try to understand them better and even to help them overcome their problem.

Some of the questions asked by interested management or union officials can now be answered as a result of the work of biological and social scientists. They point out that persons in the early and middle phases of alcoholism continue to work on full-time, regular jobs at all occupational levels, usually with sharply impaired efficiency. Because of the number of employees involved, employers are realizing that employees in the previously unrecognized early and middle stages of alcoholism—the "problem-drinking" phase—constitute a personnel problem they cannot afford to overlook.

Several well-known companies pioneered in the rehabilitation of alcoholic employees through referral to Alcoholics Anonymous and medical treatment at clinics. These employers are convinced that this is a more constructive approach to the problem than carrying unidentified, inefficient workers on the payroll for years and finally replacing them when they become obviously alcoholic.

Although other aspects of the problem of alcoholism have received considerable attention in current literature, there has been little emphasis on the *job* aspects. How far along in the alcoholism process are employed "problem drinkers"? What are their age, sex, and occupational characteristics? Why do people become problem drinkers? How many are employed and how much do they cost industry? How do they act on the job? What has been done, and is being done, by various companies about them? Finally, what can management do to attack the illness constructively? These are some of the questions considered here.

From management's viewpoint, a "problem drinker" is any employee whose repeated overindulgence in alcoholic beverages sharply reduces his or her effectiveness and dependability in carrying out a work assignment. A problem drinker is usually regarded as being in the earlier stages of alcoholism. Such an employee often wastes much of his time and energy merely in getting through the workday without a drink or in covering up the fact that he is drinking during working hours. His fatigue, absenteeism, uneven work pace, and mistakes not only result in poor quality and quantity of his own work, but also affect the productivity and morale of his associates. Inferior job performance and its detection vary according to occupation. The alcoholic salesman may work in spurts to try for a time to maintain his quota, whereas the assembly-line worker's increased scrap rate may easily be detected at the end of each work shift.

"Problem drinkers" by definition, however, should not be confused with such chronic users of alcohol as the "skid-row" type who are in the last and most serious stages of alcoholism, although such people, if still employed, certainly present a problem to management. The employed problem drinker does not yet have the "shakes" so badly he cannot lift his coffee cup in the morning. He has not reached the point of hiding his supply of liquor in bizarre places so he will have it available at all times. The horrors of delirium tremens are also still to be experienced by the problem drinker. A person in the early and middle stages of alcoholism may, happily, never reach the late stage, but he is certainly running the risk of it. If he does become a full-blown alcoholic he is so obvious he cannot work regularly at any job.

Neither is the problem drinker the week-end, "heavy" drinker, nor the occasionally excessive user who intermittently suffers a bad hangover. He has already gone through these drinking patterns. Now, psychological, physiological, and social changes have brought him to the point where he cannot set limits to his use of alcohol. He is well on the road to chronic alcoholism, but not there yet.

Because the problem drinker's symptoms are not so obvious as those of the chronic, final-stage alcoholic, it is harder for management to detect him. He has found ways of appearing, to an outside observer, "normal." He goes to great lengths to deny both to himself and to those who work with him that there is anything wrong. In his cover-up tactics he often has the help of work associates. The foreman, the executive, the family doctor, and the shop steward tend to think he is a "swell guy who drinks a little too much." They are often unaware of his drinking pattern, and even if they are aware of it, they do not see any dramatic signs because the changes that signal chronic alcoholism come on gradually, almost imperceptibly, over a period of years. As a result the problem drinker is usually able to work on a regular job for years without detection while he approaches the chronic stage.

In short, a "problem drinker" is an early or middle-stage alcoholic. His symptoms are not the dramatic ones of late-stage alcoholism which most people think of when they hear the term "alcoholic." Consequently, he may go unrecognized and continue to work actively at his job or profession for years, even though he is already obsessed with alcohol. It is this unrecognized, covered-up employee with a drinking problem who constitutes an especially difficult personnel problem for management.

Still other characteristics tend to prevent his identification as a developing alcoholic. In many respects an incipient alcoholic employee is like any other employee. Apparently he cannot be distinguished by his type of job, level of responsibility or skill, length of service, or by his marital status or mode of residence. Although his drinking exceeds accepted limits he is still part of established social and economic patterns of living.

Recent research on the problem drinker shows him to be more stable, socially and occupationally, than early studies did. An analysis of the records of over 2,000 male patients at nine alcoholism clinics shows that 86 per cent of them had lived in the town of their present residence for at least two years; 75 per cent resided in their own home or that of relatives or friends as contrasted with a rooming house, hotel, or institution; and 53 per cent were married and living with their wives.[1] Sixty-nine per cent of 830 patients at a private hospital for alcoholics were married and living with their wives.[2]

At the time of their first visit to the clinic 62 per cent of the patients were employed; 95 per cent of the private hospital patients were employed. Over half of the clinic patients had held a steady job for at least three years; a fourth had held one for at least ten years.

Employers' reports confirm these service records. Two-thirds of 71 alcoholic cases at Allis-Chalmers had been employed five to fifteen years.[3] At Consolidated Edison, the average length of services of the 183 employees in the company alcoholism program during 1952-1955 was 22 years.[4]

Problem drinkers are not concentrated in any one segment of the labor force. They have jobs in all industries and at all occupational levels. Both clinic and private hospital cases were employed in every type of industry. The following table shows the distribution of clinic and private patients by type of industry compared with the same distribution in the general population as reported by the U.S. Census, 1950 (in per cent).

	Clinic Patients	Private Patients	General Population
Agriculture, Fishing, Forestry	2%	17.5%	12.5%
Construction, Mining	6	7.8	7.8
Manufacturing, Transportation	31	3.1	25.9
Communication, Utilities	10	11.3	7.8
Wholesale, Retail trade	14	30.2	18.8
Finance, Real-estate, Insurance	4	3.5	3.4
Services	21	19.9	18.1
Government	10	0.7	4.4
Other	2	6.0	1.3
Total	100	100	100
Number	(1740)	(830)	(56,239,449)

Furthermore, there is no evidence that problem drinkers are more apt to be found in one occupation than another. Vice-President D.W. Ferrier of the Bell Telephone Company of Canada, after pointing out that the illness occurred no more frequently in his company than in other organizations, observed:

As has been found elsewhere . . . we in the Bell were impressed by the apparently widespread occurrence of alcoholism throughout the employee force. It was found among our craftsmen, our line crews, our foremen, and our clerks. It occurred in our middle levels of management and occasionally in the higher management group. It also occurred among our women, although with less frequency than among our men.[5]

At Consolidated Edison approximately 70 per cent of the alcoholic cases were engaged in physical work; 30 per cent were on the clerical staff.

The dispersion of problem drinkers throughout the occupational structure is also described by the data from the clinic and private hospital studies. This distribution is shown in the following table compared with the occupational distribution of the general population as reported by the 1950 Census (in per cent). Of the clinic patients, 20 per cent were from high-status job categories such as manager and professional, while 17 per cent were unskilled; the rest were distributed in the intermediate levels. A greater proportion of the patients in the private hospital were in the high-status categories and fewer were unskilled; this was to be expected since the cost the treatment was a selective factor.

Occupational Class	Clinic Patients	Private Patients	General Population
Official, manager, owner	14%	40.9%	16.6%
Professional	6	6.5	8.7
Public Servant	7	1.3	1.2
Clerical	6	2.6	12.3
Salesman	10	9.7	7.0
Skilled labor	23	9.5	13.8
Semiskilled labor	16	17.6	19.8
Unskilled labor	17	5.0	6.1
Service, other than public servant	—	—	9.0
Farm laborers and Foremen	—	—	4.2
Other	1	6.9	1.3
Total	100	100	100
Number	(1729)	(830)	(56,239,449)

A study of 200 members of Alcoholics Anonymous reported that 30 per cent of the respondents were in professional and managerial jobs; 31 per cent were in the service, semiskilled, and unskilled classifications; the remainder were in clerical, sales, and skilled occupations.[6] Again, however, the importance is not in the comparisons but in the fact that there are alcoholics at every occupational level.

Middle-stage alcoholics seem, on the other hand, to be heavily concentrated in certain age and sex categories. They are in the mature, productive years of life and most of them are men. The clinic and private hospital records both showed over 80 per cent of the men between 30 and 55 years of age. The average age of the clinic patients was 41.2 years; of the private patients, 42.6 years. Reports from industry itself indicate a slightly older age. The average Allis-Chalmers case was 44.9 years, and 70 per cent were in the 30 to 55-year range. At Consolidated Edison the average age was 47.3; 77 per cent of the cases were between 35 and 55. All studies of large groups of alcoholics show their average age between 41.2 and 47.9 years, indicating that the problem-drinking employee is in what should be his most productive years.

The high ratio of male to female alcoholics has varied only within a narrow range since 1940. In 1953 it was 5.5 to 1.[7] Even though more women are employed today than 20 years ago, the labor force is still made up chiefly of males. Consequently, incipient alcoholism occurs most frequently among those who make up the bulk of the work force, namely, male personnel.

In contrast to these fairly definite conclusions, little can be said about the actual number of problem drinkers regularly employed in the nation's labor force. Despite various speculations, there is at present no systematic way of making an estimate. Those who have made guesses regarding the extent of the problem in American industry have done so in one of two ways. Either rough guesses have been made by taking the total estimate of all kinds of alcoholics in the entire population and then assuming that a certain proportion of them are employed; or studies of the extent of the problem in specific companies have been used to indicate the possible extent in the general labor force. Obviously both methods are questionable.

The first uses the Jellinek Estimation Formula[8] as a base. This is a complex statistical device designed to estimate the total number of alcoholics alive in a given year. In 1953 this figure was slightly more than 4,500,000;[9] in 1955 it was 4,712,-000.[10] There is reason to believe that this formula has substantial accuracy. In seven out of ten independent studies of the incidence of alcoholism in specific localities there was close agreement with estimates made with the formula.[11] The big problem, assuming the accuracy of the device, lies in deciding how many of the estimated 4,712,000 cases are regularly working in the nation's labor force. At this point most observers have "played it safe" and arbitrarily said only half of this number were employed.

Specific company studies have reported estimates varying from less than 1 per cent up to 10 per cent of their personnel.[12] Such a wide variation does not permit speculation on the number throughout the economy. These figures have, however, been interpreted by observers to mean that at least 3 per cent of the working population are probably problem drinkers.

In sum, these approaches have given rise to a belief that there are approximately two million regularly employed, middle-stage alcoholics in American businesses and industries. Although the number may be considerably more, or less, than this figure, it is clear that there are many problem-drinking employees spread throughout the various occupations and industries of America. They are first-class personnel problems and usually present their employers with a unique and difficult situation.

NOTES

1. R. Straus and S. D. Bacon, "Alcoholism and Social Stability: A Study of Occupational Integration in 2,023 Male Clinic Patients," *Quarterly Journal of Studies on Alcohol,* Vol. 12, 1951, pp. 231-260.

2. W. M. Wellman, M. A. Maxwell, and P. O'Hollaren, "Private Hospital Alcoholic Patients and the Changing Conception of the 'Typical' Alcoholic," *Quarterly Journal of Studies on Alcohol,* Vol. 18, 1957, pp. 388-404.

3. *Results to Date—March 15, 1950—Allis-Chalmers Alcoholic Program* (Milwaukee, Wis.: Allis-Chalmers Manufacturing Co.).

4. S. C. Franco, "Problem Drinking in Industry: Review of a Company Program," *Industrial Medicine and Surgery,* Vol. 26, 1957, pp. 221-228.

5. D. W. Ferrier, "Management Policy and the Alcoholic," an address to the Ontario Alcoholism Research Foundation, Ottawa, Ontario, Oct. 31, 1953.

6. Trice, H. M., "Absenteeism Among High-Status and Low-Status Problem Drinkers," *ILR Research,* Vol. IV, No. 1, Spring 1958, pp. 10-13.

7. M. Keller and V. Efron, "The Prevalence of Alcoholism," *Quarterly Journal of Studies on Alcohol,* Vol. 16, 1955, pp. 619-644.

8. "Jellinek Estimation Formula", in *Expert Committee on Mental Health,* Report on the First Session of the Alcoholism Subcommittee, World Health Organization, Technical Series No. 42 (Geneva, 1951), pp. 21-24.

9. M. Keller and V. Efron, "The Prevalence of Alcoholism," *Quarterly Journal of Studies on Alcohol,* Vol. 16, 1955, pp. 619-644.

10. Mark Keller, "Alcoholism, Nature and Extent of the Problem," *Annals of the American Academy of Political and Social Science,* Vol. 315, 1958, pp. 1-11.

11. E. R. Popham, "The Jellinek Alcoholism Estimation Formula and Its Application to Canadian Data," *Quarterly Journal of Studies on Alcohol,* Vol. 17, 1956, pp. 559-593.

12. C. C. O'Brien, "Alcoholism Among Disciplinary Cases in Industry," *Quarterly Journal of Studies on Alcohol,* Vol. 10, 1949, pp. 268-278; R. C. Page, J. J. Thorpe, and D. W. Caldwell, "The Problem Drinker in Industry," *Quarterly Journal of Studies on Alcohol,* Vol. 13, 1952, pp. 370-396; S. C. Franco, "Problem Drinking in Industry: Review of a Company Program," *Industrial Medicine and Surgery,* Vol. 26, 1957, p. 223; M. Cruickshank, "Industry Has a Responsibility Here," *Alcoholism Research,* Vol. 2, No. 3, 1955; R. Straus, "Recognizing the Problem Drinker in Business and Industry," *Journal of Business,* Vol. 25, 1952, pp. 95-100; Lewis F. Presnall, "Alcoholism: A Workable Program in Industry," Chino Mines Division of Kennecott Copper Corporation, 1956, mimeo.

15 Who Becomes a Problem Drinker?

A very important question, and the most difficult one to answer, is: why do some employees become problem drinkers? The answers are very controversial, and only recently have scientific efforts been made to determine the causes.

Before the late thirties practically all speculation was colored by the white-heat emotions of the "wet" versus the "dry" battle. The wets argued that there were always a few who would abuse anything, that some people were "born that way" and if it wasn't alcohol it would be something else. The drys said the alcoholic was lacking in will power, that he was irresponsible, weak, and morally degenerate, and only the complete prohibition of alcohol would protect him. In the last two decades, answers to the question have tended to ignore this battle; yet, to a degree, the conflict has moved to the scientific arena where researchers from various fields actively debate how to explain the problem drinker.

Three explanations to consider are those of: (1) the physiologists, who believe that the inebriate has physical deficiencies; (2) the psychologists, who insist that he is emotionally unstable; and (3) the sociologists, who explain him as a result of group experiences in which he has learned to use alcohol as the way to meet his troubles. Actually, a fourth approach is crystallizing. It tries to find out how the physical, emotional, and group aspects work together, rather than separately, to produce the disorder.

Numerous researchers who specialize in the study of human physiology explain the behavior in question in terms of bodily need. They usually describe this need in dietary terms: that a nutritional deficiency from birth creates a need for rapidly oxidized foodstuffs; or that there is damage to the bodily mechanism which converts most foods to energy. Alcohol can temporarily fill such a need because it is converted into energy more rapidly than other foodstuffs and by a different metabolic process. This alternative method is learned in the process of social drinking. However, most of the research data for this explanation has come from experiments on rats, mice, cats, and monkeys.

The physiologist's explanation cannot be accepted unless he is able to answer several basic questions. First, since human beings have poor instinctive equipment and the learning process often plays a vital role that overshadows the biological process, can these findings based on research on animals be applied to humans? Second, can it be demonstrated where in the human anatomy this assumed deficiency exists? Finally, if the deficiency does exist, does it necessarily lead to disruptive drinking, or could not other foodstuffs be selected to meet this peculiar body need?

Many psychiatrists and psychologists insist that unstable emotions underlie inebriety, that those who use alcohol excessively are persons who cannot stand strain, tension, or anxiety. Many developing alcoholics, they say, use it to blot out temporarily the realization of failure. All alcoholics are presumed to be immature persons who cannot persevere and who are unable to meet new responsibilities. Some are alleged to use alcohol to dissolve feelings of guilt which result from their conflicts over how to conduct themselves. Others, psychologists claim, find in it a way to relieve their tensions as nursing did when they were infants.

Although these explanations are popularly accepted, they are not without defects. None of these researchers has clearly demonstrated that the alcoholic is more immature or has more fixations and guilt feelings than persons who do not have a drinking problem. Nor have they shown whether or not these unstable emotions existed before he became a problem drinker. Psychological or psychiatric testing takes place after the disorder has started, and it cannot be assumed that what is found at that time necessarily existed before the problem developed. Unstable emotions may be the result rather than the cause of drinking.

Sociologists say that the problem drinker can be best explained by the characteristics of the groups in which he participates. These characteristics determine his attitude toward alcohol. According to this point of view a person may learn in the groups to which he belongs to use alcohol in such a way as to have little or no bearing on his personal problems. For example, the Orthodox Jews, in connection with religious ceremonies, use alcohol freely, yet alcoholism is rare among them. It is difficult to believe that these people would not have their expected quota of persons with physical deficiencies and unstable emotions. The sociologists conclude that they have group controls by means of which excessive use is prevented.

In contrast, according to this view, the problem drinker has learned what alcohol means in groups with entirely different attitudes toward drinking. In such groups alcohol is used as *the way* to adjust to anxiety and difficulties; drinking behavior is often given group prestige. Once conditioned to use alcohol as a way to manage the ever-present problems of living, it is a simple step to increase its use when problems become greater.

The high problem-drinking rate among the Irish is, according to sociologists, a classic example of this type of group conditioning which induces members to "drink their troubles away."

As with the others, there are also shortcomings in this explanation. Most of the evidence for it comes from second-hand rather than first-hand analysis of drinking groups. Furthermore, there are many persons who are conditioned by such drinking groups as the Irish who do not develop a drinking problem. Another objection to this answer lies in its broad generalizations. To a marked degree, sociologists have had to rely on data from broad categories, such as religious, occupational, and social classes, for their explanation. These classifications are vague and leave room for the influence of many non-social factors.

The best explanation of the incipient alcoholic, according to another school of thought, lies in a combination of these approaches. It is contended that probably no single factor would lead to problem drinking, and, in fact, proponents of the physiological, emotional, and group approaches recognize this fact. Obviously, the causes may be operating in different proportions in different cases, but no one alone is likely to explain a drinking problem. One of the emotional problems of the developing alcoholic may be that he has a higher than usual anxiety concerning what others think of him and how he stands competitively. It is also quite probable that physical defects may join emotional factors to build up a strong potential toward alcoholism. But the mere presence of these does not automatically mean uncontrolled drinking.

Group experiences appear to serve as the link between these physiological and emotional inclinations and the excessive use of alcohol. The problem drinker learns by repeated usage that alcohol can act as a means of adjustment. Such learning, for many persons, takes place in groups in which they grow up and to which they are attracted. Many drinking groups emphasize alcohol as a temporary solution for personal troubles. The sensitive person who is attracted to such groups often learns to lean on alcohol. It brings him two rewards: his anxiety is reduced and he is accepted by a friendly group. He can get, however, not only acceptance and reward from the drinking group, but also rejection by "going too far." If the problem drinker is excluded from the group for his drinking exploits, this is a further anxiety and is almost always met by a technique already well known—more alcohol.

On the other hand, there are definite exceptions to this general explanation, especially when some types of alcoholics are considered. There is the "loner," an alcoholic in whom group factors apparently played a minor role. There are the mentally ill—paranoids and manic depressives, for example— whose excessive drinking is symptomatic of their well-defined emotional pathology.

Evidence indicates, however, that industry and business will most frequently encounter the problem drinker who is a mixture of emotional, physiological, and group forces rather than the symptomatic alcoholic whose addiction is due almost solely to an unusual emotional or physiological factor. Some problem drinkers, it is true, practically begin their drinking histories with solitary drinking. Most, however, start as social drinkers and experience a long period of drinking-group activity before their isolated drinking begins.

Even among alcoholics who have been frequently hospitalized, the psychotic or deeply neurotic alcoholic is still in the minority. An intensive review of 161 such cases showed 60 per cent did not fit any usual psychiatric diagnosis. The majority of these cases were primarily alcoholics and did not suffer from the typical kinds of mental illnesses.

In short, the problem drinker appears to be most often the product of the three factors mentioned above working in combination. He no doubt has emotional problems, but apparently they do not differ from those of many nonalcoholics. It also seems likely that he had physiological potential for addiction to alcohol. But these various predispositions do not seem to be, in and of themselves, strong enough to bring about alcoholism. When combined with group influences, however, physical and emotional inclinations result in the excessive use of alcohol.

16 The Role of Business in Arresting Alcoholism

Developing alcoholics in the early and early-middle stages of the disorder continue to work actively at a job. So they are regularly in and on-going situation where they are visible to bosses, fellow workers, and union people. Thus the early and middle symptoms of alcoholism can be seen and identified on the job. It is true that the earliest signs are skillfully covered at work by the alcoholic employee. But as the middle symptoms begin to appear they are readily visible. It is also true that certain jobs are mobile, somewhat isolated, and often free from supervision. But these are a small minority of jobs. Most jobs by their very nature—schedules, routines, inspection—act to expose clues of alcoholism.

It is not difficult for a supervisor to observe a repeated decline in work performance. At first it will be spotty; as the illness progresses, overall work effectiveness will decline. Indeed, the boss can hardly fail to notice it in most cases. Various forms of absenteeism, including unusual kinds such as leaving a job for a sizable block of time, are equally obvious.

At first the boss will not notice too much and the alcoholic employee will go to great lengths to cover up, but, again, signs will soon become apparent. For example, he will notice the unusual excuses that pile up to explain absences—even to the point of flagrant, open lies. The same could be said for mood changes after drinking—especially after noontime drinking—for spasmodic work pace, and for such physical clues as red or bleary eyes, hand tremors, and flushed face.

Indeed, it is difficult to accept the oft-heard description of the "hidden" alcoholic on the job. Beyond doubt the earliest signs are not too visible, are well covered by the employee. But relatively soon, various clues begin to appear on the job. These are correspondingly early in the illness so they can help identify the illness at a time when therapy has a better chance of succeeding.

Of course, the term "hidden" may well be true of executive alcoholics who have excellent opportunities to camouflage themselves. The same might be said for doctors and scientists who work in industry. But for the majority it is difficult to see how their developing alcoholism can be hidden for very long from those in direct, regular day-to-day contact with them. Higher echelons of management may not observe them. Staff people who are also removed from the specific work place may likewise be unaware of them. But their immediate supervisors and face-to-face fellow workers in all likelihood observe many of the on-the-job signs of alcoholism in its earlier forms.

It is less likely that those close to the problem drinker on the job will always connect what they observe with incipient alcoholism. On the other hand there is a good chance that such linkage can be made. It is not too difficult to "put two and two together," although errors are a hazard. It is reasonable to say, however, that training can aid in bringing about an awareness of what various alcoholism signs mean.

A second reason why the work world can greatly contribute to recovery from alcoholism is its emphasis on performance.

Because doing a good job—"getting the job done"—is a core value in the work world, it is in a unique position to define early and middle symptoms as undesirable and disruptive. One of the chief job characteristics of employed alcoholics is their repeated poor work. So the malady produces a direct violation of a basic work value. This gives all levels of management a clear basis for entering an employee's private life. It gives the union a simple reason to join with managmement in support of a treatment policy.

Recurrent poor job performance due to the use of alcohol becomes, for industry, a simple, direct, and clear indication of alcoholism. Compared with the definitions of the clinic and research project, this is the essence of simplicity. It avoids the complex. As such it is easily understood by busy supervisors as well as the alcoholic employee himself. Alcoholism simply causes repeated poor work because of the way the employee uses alcohol. This in turn has a bad effect on smooth job operations as far as the boss, peers, and union representatives are concerned.

By using this simple key to what alcoholism involves, two very basic things happen. First, the behavior is seen as *undesirable*. This characterization does not come from home or church, but from an unsentimental, practical, "hard-headed," work world. It does not provide any prestige at all for the early and middle symptoms of alcoholism as is often the case. Rather it "calls a spade a spade" in a simple manner, linking it with easily understood job behavior.

Secondly, it helps "clear the air" generally. Americans have been traditionally mixed up about alcohol, both praising and blaming it for all kinds of results. Characterizations of alcoholism—especially those that include the earlier symptoms—have suffered from this confusion. Industry has the unique opportunity to provide clarity by being firm and consistent in considering alcoholism as recurrent unsatisfactory job performance due to the use of alcohol. In addition, a wide-spread use of such an interpretation would help reduce the historical "wet-dry" battle over alcohol. This tradition struggle has produced a moralizing, crusading atmosphere. The calm, detached tone of the job-oriented description acts to put the behavior in an illness category where it can be treated rather than argued about.

A third feature of business and industry makes them especially able to cope with alcoholism. Because the work place is typically organized around *authority,* this description of alcoholism can be given to any alcoholic employee in an atmosphere of "constructive coercion." In other words, not only can there be a simple, easily-understood characterization, but there can be tied to it an inevitable result should alcoholism continue: *job loss.*

Applied in an impersonal fashion, but underscoring a positive offer of help as its main feature, this sanction is probably the most readily available way for getting the developing alcoholic to face up to his problem. Obviously, such use of authority must be tailored to the individual differences of specific cases. Also obvious is the fact that this approach is not a cure-all. But compared to possible action by home or church it probably has more "teeth" in it. So it must be ranked very high among available tools. *In short, an effective approach to the problem of alcoholism calls for the development of new, authoritative group sanctions.* Job-centered definitions, treatment, and sanctions offer an excellent source in our society for these needed forces.

Never believe that the job is no longer important in a person's life, nor that its loss is easily accepted. Work, and the work place, continue to play an important role for Americans, especially men. Despite a widespread reduction of the skill content of jobs, they still occupy a central position in our lives. Eighty per cent of a recent national sample of adult men said they would continue to work even if they could get along easily without working. In addition, retirement often brings with it a sense of loss at no longer performing a job. This feeling occurs among employees in a wide range of occupations. Both of these points show the value of the job in the lives of large numbers of people. Finally, unemployment is obviously demoralizing, showing thereby the importance of being employed.

In addition to emotional needs for work, there are also increased economic benefits in the job. "Fringes" of every conceivable kind have been added to the cash incomes of millions of jobs. Seniority due to union membership adds a second economic investment. It represents in the minds of many employees a degree of job ownership similar to home ownership after years of mortgage payments.

While the emotional and economic values of jobs remain high, so does the work routine and discipline that organizes them. Thus in manufacturing and retail trades the number of planners, supervisors, schedulers, and coordinators is growing. On large numbers of jobs the timing and sequence of tasks has never been so specifically spelled out for the employee. Not only does the typical employee have many investments in the job; he usually does his job in a network of controls and routine. These usually make his work behavior highly visible to bosses and fellow workers.

A developing alcoholic is therefore usually unable to treat a job threat lightly, especially if it is connected with constructive chances for treatment. He knows that the results of his alcoholism can be seen and defined due to work routines and disciplines. For once in the progress of his illness he faces a situation he cannot manipulate or stall. Many potential behavior problems are held in check by such firm, easily understood social pressures, even though there is still some emotional crippling as a result.

Finally, such sanctions, and the treatment offer linked to them, can reach a mass of developing alcoholics provided there is widespread acceptance by industry and business. Compared with such agencies as welfare and social services, the work world can influence and educate literally millions.

But all is not impersonal, cold-blooded authority on the job by any means. The work world contains one of the most important, emotionally charged relationships in practically everyone's life—the MAN-BOSS RELATIONSHIP. Here is an agent almost without peer for identifying, defining, and applying a policy of "constructive coercion" to alcoholism. As such, the supervisor, regardless of his level in management, is a fourth reason why the work world can play such a big part in attacking alcoholism.

With all due respect to spouses, it can be reasonably concluded that of the various non-alcoholic relationships in his life, the man-boss relationship has the most promise for "doing something" effective about the problem-drinking employee. In a fair number of cases he is without a spouse; indeed, he may be without relatives of any kind.

Why is the man-boss situation of such importance? The boss of a developing alcoholic takes the brunt of alcoholism on the job. It is he who must frequently face the unpleasant problems of replacements for absenteeism, of poor job performance, and of fear of incidents. It is he who never knows what to expect and so has one employee less to reply on when he plans his work. Could we get inside the head of this boss we would probably hear him say: "If I had two like this guy it would drive me nuts, and if I had three I would ask for early retirement." In other words, there is a readiness to act in his practical, on-going situation that just isn't available anywhere else.

Furthermore, most bosses of alcoholics do not engage in deliberate, willful cover-up of the condition. They may for a short time, but soon they are pressured in two directions at the same time—toward helping the worker manage the problem, on the one hand, and toward "reporting" him, on the other. So most bosses of alcoholics are ripe for help from their companies and usually welcome a way out of their dilemma.

The difficult spot the boss of an alcoholic employee finds himself in is underscored when the impact of alcoholism on the job is compared with other behavior disorders. Neuroses and psychoses, for example, often do not affect the job as much as we are prone to believe. Or, if they do, it is in a sudden, dramatic incident about which there can be no indecision: they only action left open to the supervisor is removal from the job for a long time for treatment.

But the alcoholic employee often presents a frustrating mixture of poor work and able performance, charming and disagreeable personality, hard work and rank negligence. The boss's-eye view is one of effective job performance mixed with an annoying, unpredictable loss of effectiveness and dependability. He never knows what to expect. But just when he believes his "headache" is intolerable, his problem-drinking worker "snaps out of it" and looks good again. Nothing like this tug of war starts when the supervisor works with the neurotic or even the psychotic. The response to them is usually a consistent one, regardless of whether it is favorable or unfavorable. This probably helps to explain why many companies rank alcoholism above these mental illnesses as a personnel problem—some at a 2 to 1 rate.

Matters aren't improved much for the boss by the prospect of early discharge, transfer, or quitting. Despite the highly publicized firing of alcoholics, they show no unusual job-changing features when compared with non-alcoholics in the same occupations. In short, early and middle-stage alcoholics are not "job hoppers" in any unusual way. In practical terms the immediate supervisor is more often than not "stuck." If the illness is not arrested, the alcoholic may eventually get fired, but it will then be too late for it to do much good.

In sum, the impact of alcoholism on the job situation is considerable. It centers around the difficulties of the immediate boss and of poor work. Since industry and business regard supervisors as a major asset and work production as a basic value, they have strong reasons for considering alcoholism a personnel problem. To these major factors can be added numerous other problems. There is a proportionate number of alcoholics among management personnel. But their impact on the company is far greater than the effect of non-managerial personnel who are alcoholic. The effect of the alcoholic manager on the lives of many people makes the problem among them far more acute. Finally, there are many non-alcoholic employees whose work performance is damaged by an alcoholic spouse—worry about him or her, absenteeism because of caring for spouse, etc.

A final reason why the work world can contribute greatly to the treatment of alcoholics is because it can bring to bear the influence of two potent institutions—management *and* unions —at the same time. If both of these can confront the problem in a collective manner, there is a combined force that is available nowhere else in our society.

Together, these two influences in many employees' lives offer the most concentrated possibility for action we have. True, home and church, in combination, can often exert a decided influence on the alcoholic. But their influence is also more intermittent, less immediate, and often without the impersonal authority of union combined with management.

The union member tends to see the union as a means of protection on the job. The alcoholic who is a union member thinks of manipulating this protection to his advantage. If he confronts a situation where the union tells him, in effect, the same thing his supervisor tells him, he is more likely to reconsider his situation and accept the treatment offered him. Above all, if the union will not challenge management in administering a constructive policy, then the alcoholic employee cannot play one against the other. Far better, of course, is the joint use of a similar policy.

But how can these job influences be turned into specific action? It is clear that the work world can offer much. It is also clear that the potential has not been used as much as it could —compared with efforts to use facilities such as welfare agencies, courts, and hospitals. In short, there has been a tendency to use facilities that work from a late-stage focus, reflecting a skid-row image and stigma.

On the other hand, there has been a definite start made toward effective industrial action. Many individual companies have mature programs, having developed a treatment approach as much as fifteen years ago. Still others are exploring, considering, experimenting. There are no signs that those companies who started programs have dropped them; indeed, some are currently expanding them. Specialized industrial groups, such as industrial physicians, are growing more interested yearly.

In other words, the potential present in the work world shows every sign of being realized more fully. Beyond doubt the immediate future will see the role of industry expand sharply. Now that a substantial number of companies have successfully developed a treatment approach many others are showing an interest.

Although there are many ways to express a company program on alcoholism, there are certain necessities common to all approaches. Each of these factors are necessary, but no one of them operating alone is sufficient to bring substantial results. The parts of a successful program are:

1. Personnel policy;
2. Available therapy;

3. Early identification knowledge;
4. Willingness of supervisors to use a policy and program;
5. Acceptance of treatment by alcoholic employee;
6. Long-term operation of the program;

The following pages will explore each of these parts, emphasizing their dependency on each other. It is obvious that, for example, willingness of the immediate supervisor of an alcoholic employee to use a company program is of little value unless he has the support of a clearly-stated, well-communicated company policy. Similarly, without treatment facilities there is little value in early case finding. *In other words, to be effective any program needs to recognize the dependence of these various parts on each other so that a total effort is made, not a piecemeal one.*

But immediately it should be noted that such an effort does not call for any unusual investment of time, money, or personnel. Indeed, in many ways there is no need for any at all. Personnel policy exists in any organization by the very fact that it is an on-going organization. A policy on alcoholism is merely an addition to that already present body of policy. Therapy is often available from community facilities for only a nominal charge. If not, many companies already have medical personnel who can become knowledgeable. Early-case-finding knowledge can easily be incorporated into supervisory and managerial training. In one way or another most companies engage in such training.

Training situations also contain the opportunity to motivate supervisors. A realistic discussion, using conference leadership and case methods, can aim directly at how the typical supervisor reacts to an alcoholic employee. Literature for such training is available at modest costs.

Certainly it is not costly to approach and try to motivate the employee who suffers from alcoholism. It is a part of the supervisory role to work with, understand, and help employees with their personal problems. The strategy that will work requires a different approach than is usually used, but can easily be understood. Finally, it costs very little, especially when compared with overall costs of such employees, to sustain a program for a substantial period of time. Since it involves only a modest investment to begin with, it will cost very little to continue. In addition, the return in personnel salvage can be expected to increase with time.

17 Basic Company Policy

In formulating a company policy, certain basics need to be considered:

1. Top management must define alcoholism among its employees as a health problem, requiring therapy.

2. The company intends to take a treatment attitude toward this health problem among its employees, offering assistance in securing therapy.

3. But after a reasonable opportunity for progress, job dismissal will definitely occur unless there is noticeable improvement in work.

4. This basic policy will be communicated widely, with full approval, by policy-making officers.

Naturally, any individual company will tailor these basic points to its own particular situation and conditions. Current company programs show a wide variety of ways to express these essentials. The four basics are, however, essential if a company wants to form a constructive policy toward the difficult personnel problem of alcoholism.

But there are also specific strategies that will help launch these basics. If there is a labor union in the company, its inclusion in some way at the earliest moment in forming and issuing the basic policy will make its use much simpler later. It is most helpful if the policy at first gives the alcoholism program independent status among personnel policies, but gradually blends it with general health policies as it becomes understood and accepted. The alcoholism policy should be carefully scrutinized to reduce any hint of "crusading" or unnecessary fanfare. In this connection it should take pains to distinguish between heavy drinking and alcoholism. To carry this out the policy should state its reliance on recurring on-the-job clues. Such considerations will probably raise the need to clarify the company's attitude toward alcohol in job-related situations. It is helpful to state clearly how the company regards the role of alcohol in job performance and in informal company life.

Finally, a policy is more effectively launched if it recognizes that one of its chief goals, if not its main goal, is to help the immediate supervisor of an alcoholic case. The policy is aimed at helping him cope with and motivate such an employee to accept treatment. An adjunct of this approach is the need to state that support for a supervisor by the immediate chain of command just above him is imperative.

Once formed and stated, there remains the question of spelling out how it will actually work—the mechanics that implement as well as communicate it. Will there be a formal procedure? How will coordination of effort be carried out? How are final decisions made? How will "lip-service" be avoided? These are mechanical questions that a policy must spell out.

At the same time, a policy should have its own communication procedures. Will a company-wide, mass-communications approach be used? What role will the medical. department play? Where and by whom will training be done?

In broad outline this is the overview of an ideal personnel policy on alcoholic employees. It is, however, too sketchy for practical use—it is only a skeleton on which there is little meat. So it is appropriate to fill it in with more detail about policy content, strategy, and use.

First, what are the reasons behind the "basics"? There need be no question about alcoholism being a health problem of a severe nature. As the disorder progresses there are both physical and psychological symptoms that mark the disorder as crippling. For example, appetite is badly damaged. Withdrawal symptoms, or hangovers, slowly become very pronounced, leaving the sufferer unable to concentrate on the job. He begins to be grossly untruthful to the point of complete self-deception. His self-hate produces guilt so that he works spasmodically, in spurts.

In short, he is sick in numerous ways. Probably the most obvious part of the illness is his lack of ability to control his drinking short of definite drunkenness. Thus his illness is not a matter of moral weakness, but a condition in which he is literally unable to stop drinking once he starts. A practical expression of this diagnosis is the sharp trend in the direction of accepting alcoholism as a disease by those who provide insurance coverage. It is, however, an illness with many aspects and so does not easily fit into the traditional psychiatric label. As a matter of fact, it is better to avoid such names and think rather in terms of "alcoholism," or "problem drinking."

At first, the alcoholic employee avoids absenteeism, but as his disease continues his absences mount sharply. At the same time there is a tendency for alcohol-related illnesses to increase. Upper respiratory disorders, plus various forms of gastritis are numerous and continue to be aggravated by repeated use of alcohol. At this point his drinking is clearly deviant—sharply increased and at unusual times and occasions. Job performance declines as these symptoms appear and his immediate boss must deal repeatedly with a difficult supervisory problem that makes undue demands on his time.

The second "basic"—that the company will help the alcoholic employee find treatment aid, but that if it does not produce reasonable results discharge will result—rests squarely on the impact of the illness on the work situation. There are substantial numbers of sufferers in practically all companies —3 per cent is a good figure. They have frequently been good, capable employees, except for their alcoholism.

Their presence, however, hampers smooth operation of the work unit. So the policy indicates the intention of the company to help the victims of such a disorder seek treatment. elaborate psychoanalysis is probably unnecessary. Often a fair adjustment to life can be made without unusual treatment. The policy implies the company will make an effort to identify, motivate, and, in some manner, make reasonable treatment facilities available. It implies they will do it in much the same way they would for cancer, heart trouble, and other basic illnesses.

But this treatment opportunity is offered against a clear, often repeated background: if there is no progress, if a reasonable prognosis is not fulfilled, the alcoholic will be fired, *without hesitation or vacillation*—the third "basic." Even though this is negative motivation it has some definite possibilities. There are often numerous kinds of job investments that he has made, such as seniority. Loss of income is also a difficult prospect to face. Typically, he has been able to manipulate his environment so that he could avoid clear-cut definitions of his condition. Now, however, he is faced with an unalterable fact of life. This may well be the first step in his motivation to accept his problem. In the argot of Alcoholics Anonymous, he is being helped to "hit bottom."

But he is not put in a permanent position of being labeled alcoholic by any means. Uppermost in the policy is an emphasis on a way out. As a part of company procedure he can give up his alcoholic classification without permanent labeling. By responding to the therapy offered and improving his work performance he can re-enter normal work life. Thus he is not trapped into a label that is beyond removal.

The individual nature of the prognosis should always be kept in mind when considering this "basic." It may be necessary to resort to discharge for one case on the basis of individual differences in progression, physical health, etc., yet retain a second employee because his prognosis is less favorable and requires more time. This point needs careful emphasis since it may not look like equal treatment for all. It is at this point that the industrial physician plays his most crucial role. The policy must rely on his professional standing to explain discharge action or lack of it.

These basics help immeasurably to define a condition that has probably been poorly defined in the past. Early symptoms are not seen in our society as indicating the possibility of an illness. Many of them are actually rewarded with prestige rather than looked upon as undesirable symptoms of a severe health problem. For example, drinking others "under the table" is often looked upon with favor as showing one can "hold his liquor." Actually it is a sign that the risk of becoming an alcoholic has gone up.

So if a company forms and uses a simple, straightforward policy defining alcoholism as a difficult health problem about which it will provide realistic help, it will, in effect, be reducing the confusion. Actually, our whole society is confused over what alcohol should mean. It is both revered and damned. The same quandry characterizes reaction to the developing alcoholic. As a result there is usually floundering and indecision on the part of those around him, permitting him to progress more and more into the disorder. Any company which simply defines alcoholism as a health problem that should be treated—but with definite discharge to result if progress does not take place—is making a solid contribution to clarity.

But unless these basics are announced openly in writing by top policy-making officials of a company, they lose much of their force—the fourth "basic." There is a formal authority structure in practically all companies that must put its *full* weight behind such a policy change before it will be recognized and acted upon. Indications that this backing is lacking can be very crippling. This authority provides the cornerstone for supervisory action and for motivating the alcoholic employee himself. There is a tendency for supervision to be indecisive, so the policy needs to be emphatically stated and consistently supported. Otherwise informal practices can make it void even though it is formally stated. Also there is a definite possibility that mere lip service will creep in—this danger underscores further the need for a strong, emphatic, fully-supported policy statement, written out clearly and widely circulated.

But this basic policy can be launched with more chance of success if certain strategic actions and positions are taken, as outlined above. The need to give the policy independent standing among other personnel policies for a substantial amount of time is prominent among them. Because of the traditional confusion and emotion over alcoholism, there is a tendency to shunt it to one side, to ignore it. Resistance in many quarters is "par for the course." Members of management are apt to say: "I have heard, but I do not accept." So it is necessary to give the policy independence and a degree of spotlighting for a reasonable time. In other words, give it its rightful place for a sufficient time for it to become widely understood and acted upon.

At the same time, it is important to avoid as much as possible all signs of crusading and overzealousness. It is very easy when writing such a policy to fall into a moralizing, latter day prohibitionism. It is well to launch such a policy within limited management circles first, expanding its communication steadily to all segments of the company. In other words, it is often best to prove a policy first, i.e., develop it quietly before there is issuance of a formal statement.

A good case can also be made for avoiding mass publicity outside the company. This merely adds to the possibility of the policy being seen as a revival of the wet-dry struggle in a new garb. The slogan could well be: "Quietly, but firmly and without fanfare." Too much publicity can lead to charges of coddling, which, in turn, may bring about a tightening up that produces a change before the policy has had a chance to operate. Furthermore, such tightening tends to give supervisors the fear that using a policy inevitably means discharge.

It is often desirable to wait for a favorable time to launch a policy. A rash of discipline cases involving alcoholics may make it timely. The medical department may report a rise in medical complications associated with alcohol excesses. Within management there may develop a discontent over the way some cases are summarily discharged while others are tolerated. A prominent case may develop within management circles. If the prospect of an opportune situation like one of these is good, a policy can be made to follow just after.

Next, if a union is present, the policy will be strengthened immensely if every effort is made to involve the union before and during the official launching. This does not mean that a company need include the union in its original decision to develop a policy. Most managements reject any situation where the union mught directly invade specific decision-making rights. It does mean, however, that a unionized company needs to tell the union officials as soon as possible the nature of the policy. This permits discussion and explanation of the policy.

As noted earlier the combined weight of both union and management is obviously more effective than management alone. Certainly a hostile union can cripple the practical operation of a policy if it has a false notion of it. Certainly, too, management has the right to formulate such programs and administer them as it sees fit. Decisions by the National Labor Relations Board establish this point beyond doubt: management does not have to tolerate the alcoholic employee. There are numerous precedents in the grievance procedure to show this.

But an uncooperative union can badly stall the use of a treatment policy by supervisors and employees. Bosses will become concerned about getting "mixed up with the union," while an alcoholic employee will use the union's protective role as a way to deny his drinking problem. So if management uses its legal position it will merely be defeating the treatment purpose of its policy.

It seems far better to understand how the union tends to react in such situations, and to approach the union within that framework. First, the traditional role of the union is to protect its members against alleged unfair treatment. Members expect it to go through this function, so it does. But usually they fulfill this role, where alcoholism cases are concerned, on an informal basis and tend to avoid formal grievance procedures if possible. In short, they are performing the protective function without taking a specific case too far.

If management will keep the negotiations at this level, taking pains to explain the nature of alcoholism and its policy, the union can go through its defense of the case without taking a firm stand, as it would have to do if the case went to the grievance procedure. Once there the union will be fully committed to defense, claiming such things as insufficient warning, poor diagnosis, and no measure for alleged poor performance of work. In short, rarely is anything of a therapeutic nature gained by "going formal."

Second, naturally the union wants to feel in on the policy. It wants to be able to tell the alcoholic member that it can help him get treatment and "another chance." Often, local union officials are aware of the problem and realize the futility of defending the problem drinker. But they also need an opportunity to be identified with the policy, to claim cooperation and inclusion.

They often tend to adopt a participating role if given an opportunity. They can appreciate the nature of the illness, the increased effect if there is cooperation, the need for clear job sanctions in case of poor progress. The shop steward often shares the "headache" of a problem drinker with the supervisor. Fellow members often resent this employee and make this known to the union steward.

Management can more effectively develop and begin its policy if it will realize the need of the union to be informed of developments and to be identified with them in some way. If the union is informally prepared for a policy, and if management understands the union's need informally to perform a protective function, then management's prerogatives can be fully recognized and intense union resistance can be avoided.

In such an atmosphere it is much easier to explain that the "salvage of some means the firing of some," based on individual assessment. This is probably the most difficult, practical view for unions to accept. They are much more likely to do so if they have had an opportunity to be identified with the policy at an early stage of its writing. It should be added that there may be members of Alcoholics Anonymous among union officials. If so, and if they offer their help, they can be very effective in developing an informal appreciation of a policy.

In much the same vein, a policy can be more effective if its main target is frankly recognized to be the relief and aid of the immediate boss of an alcoholic employee, as well as the helping of the employee himself. In a very realistic sense these two make up the hard core of resistance to a policy. All other parts of a program lead up to these two people. This point does not belittle other aspects of a program. It does, however, emphasize the fact that other parts operate to motivate the alcoholic and his boss to take constructive action.

Accordingly, a policy can be launched with such a view simply stated. If the other parts of a program are working they sooner or later confront these two key people. Since the supervisor bears the brunt of the alcoholism problem in an employee, he is the one who will decide whether or not to use the policy. If he is motivated to respond to a personnel policy that is fully supported by top management and which makes treatment available within well-defined limits, then the payoff has been partly realized.

There remains only the final, most difficult part of the hard core—motivating the problem-drinking employee himself. If, however, his boss is able to resolve his indecision and use the alcoholism policy, a big start has been made on the alcoholic himself.

But it also needs to be clearly realized that the immediate boss of a developing alcoholic is often on only the first, second, or third rung of the managerial ladder. Thus he is very sensitive about, and vulnerable to, attack from those above him. Unless the policy points out this dependency of supervisors on their bosses, and the need for *unit* support of a policy, it is more difficult for any particular supervisor to use the policy. Without this support "up the line" the supervisor, regardless of his desire to act, cannot feel secure in using the policy—it might blow up in his face.

A final set of strategies can aid in the way the basics of a policy are presented. It is well for the statement to emphasize the importance of detecting alcoholism early. In other words, the policy recognizes its dependence on early case-finding rather than waiting for the more obvious symptoms to develop. There is wide agreement that cases identified in the earlier period of development have a higher chance of recovery.

Such an emphasis will raise the question of the difference between the heavy drinker and the early alcoholic. A policy can simply state that such a distinction can be made, noting in passing that there are those who drink heavily and steadily for years without it impairing their work. The policy is in no way aimed at them—there is no witch-hunting involved. The only focus is on interference with job performance.

Some companies have decided to include in their policy statements a point about the role alcohol is expected to play in various jobs that might involve its use, pointing out that such jobs can be performed effectively without alcohol. On the other hand, they merely state that the company does not believe it is necessary; they conclude by giving the employee full right to decide. One company states clearly that alcohol is expected to play only a minor role in company affairs, including social functions, both formal and informal.

Still another puts a paragraph in its policy statement indicating that encouragement of heavy drinking in connection with company activities of any kind could expose personnel to alcoholism. It also made it quite clear that it was in no way a prohibition, but an attempt to underscore the risk of unintended exposure. In both of these cases it was observed that alcohol did have benefits as well as dangers—i.e., an effort to show the dangers, but also to provide the policy statement with some balance.

Following the writing of a specific policy and its effective introduction, two questions about policy still remain: How will it work, what are the procedures and mechanics? How will it be communicated? Actually these questions must be resolved before any introduction of a policy, but for discussion purposes they will be considered last.

The first procedural question is: who will identify and refer to the program? This is almost certainly the responsibility of line supervision. The immediate boss, regardless of level, will decide when work has been regularly disrupted and what clues are present indicating alcoholism. In this responsibility he can be provided the help of medical personnel who can aid him in deciding if there is a reasonable basis for believing alcoholism is present. But it is his basic responsibility to decide to use the program. It is also his responsibility to tell the alcoholic employee the nature of his disorder and what the company policy is.

The next procedural question is: how does the immediate boss get him to the available treatment? He could make referral direct to the medical department, or he could be required to work with a representative of the personnel department. In any event, one of these two must coordinate the relationship between the supervisor and the treatment situation. If an employee-counseling approach is used, whereby a variety of services, including medical, are brought into the picture, the personnel department is the logical place to which the supervisor should refer. If, however, treatment responsibility is lodged primarily in the medical department, direct referral to this unit should be made the procedure.

Whatever the choice, one point is clear, namely that coordination between line supervision and treatment must be firmly lodged in some well-established unit. This unit will receive referral cases from immediate supervision, decide on treatment type and routing, and tell the immediate boss the prognosis. It will process the treatment, whether it be in-company or outside, and report to the immediate supervisor when he can expect improvement and how much.

Next comes the procedural question: who applies the sanction if reasonable improvement is not forthcoming, i.e., who decides that discharge is necessary? Only the immediate boss, who sees day-to-day work behavior, knows whether or not the job performance of the alcoholic employee has improved. So it seems logical to lodge this responsibility with the boss. Again he can call on staff services to provide guide lines, but he makes the final decision that progress has not been made and the employee should be discharged. The coordinating unit should, however, have the responsibility of getting him to make a decision and of explaining the basic policy and individual facts of a specific case.

In short, the individual boss must be steadily reminded of assessed progress and make a decision in light of a prognosis. If the boss decides the employee has not responded to treatment offered, the coordinating unit refers to the personnel department for formal discharge, or, if the immediate boss has this authority, he discharges direct. Since discharge is infrequent in many companies, the coordinating unit should be given the responsibility to see that this action is carried out once the boss has made the decision. It is also desirable to *designate one person in the coordinating unit* to handle these various responsibilities, especially the regular communication with the immediate boss about his estimation of progress and about what a realistic prognosis is.

Once a policy has procedures spelled out, a decision must be made on the degree of formality; i.e., will detailed, written steps be set down in writing, or will the basic policy be written and communicated, allowing each administrative unit to work out specific procedures with the coordinator? This is largely a matter of general company practice. But some formality will help produce uniform action and give the coordinator more opportunity to explain the basic policy.

18 Treatment Sources

Before a policy can work it must have therapeutic techniques at hand to which the alcoholic employee can be referred. Regardless of how good the policy is, it cannot function without tangible means for treatment, either inside or outside the company, or a combination of these two.

Inside an organization, medical personnel such as physicians and nurses make up one treatment resource. Many companies, however, have only a nurse, or a physician on retainer, rather than a full-time medical department. In addition, some companies employ a trained employee counselor or psychologist. If these persons know the nature of alcoholism and have some training in the various treatment approaches they can fulfill the need for available therapy. If they do not have a suitable background they can be encouraged, even directed, to secure the necessary information. Various companies have assigned the treatment of alcoholism to a specific member of the medical department, providing him with an opportunity to contact specialists and study the literature. Still others have merely requested their medical personnel to develop treatment methods and take the initiative in learning as much as possible about therapeutic techniques. In those rare cases where a psychiatrist is a part of the medical department, he provides the treatment or treatment referral.

Fortunately, industrial physicians as a group are well aware of alcoholism as a disease. Their professional organization and literature often discuss the nature of the disorder. Information on treatment and diagnosis is readily available within professional circles. Consequently, for those companies with an industrial physician, full or part-time, a policy can find a treatment outlet quickly. Many such physicians are interested, enthusiastic, and knowledgeable. The close tie between developing alcoholism and other medical complications has made them sensitive to the disease. In all probability they welcome a realistic, straightforward policy. In one way or another they have probably been treating alcoholics for some time and already have considerable experience. The policy will give them the opportunity to treat more openly and directly.

On the other hand, a program can rely too much on the industrial physician and forget the policy. The physician can provide treatment know-how, help the supervisor who takes the initiative to use the policy, and supply the individual prognosis for each case. But he cannot substitute for a policy and its execution by all levels of management. There is a danger that an alcoholism program will come to center in one or two physicians rather than in management acting *in conjunction with* the physician or medical department.

The responsibility for treatment is a large one and can be hampered by placing the entire program primarily in the doctor's jurisdiction. Even more important is his prognostic role. When the union asks such basic questions as why management made the decision to stop therapy for one alcoholic and discharge him, but kept another on therapy, the answer must come from the physician.

In view of such responsibilities, the industrial physician needs all the help he can get from the personnel department and supervision. They too must assume responsibilities in a program: early identification and referral, plus carrying out of discharge if reasonable progress, based on the doctor's prognosis, does not develop.

In those situations where there is no full or part-time physician with a background in industrial medicine, the company usually has a doctor on retainer basis for pre-employment physicals and accident emergencies. Since the American Medical Association has officially recognized alcoholism as a disease, the company can request its physician to obtain as much information as possible about treatment techniques, specialists in the area, and clinics or information centers.

There is a growing interest and knowledge among general practitioners. On the other hand they as yet are not well-trained or informed about the disorder and it is quite possible that any specific doctor who has a general practice may hold false notions that hamper treatment rather than further it. Probably the chief problem is an unwillingness to devote the time necessary to follow through with an alcoholic case. It is well to make sure a general practitioner has an enlightened view before he is given the chief treatment responsibility.

The well-informed industrial nurse may be just as useful, if not more so, as one to represent treatment in a company without an industrial physician. She is limited by restrictions that prevent her from actual treatment in a technical sense. But she can counsel, help in early recognition, and develop detailed knowledge of referral possibilities.

Despite her limitations she has numerous advantages. She is usually full-time and so knows the work situation intimately, allowing her to notice recurrent medical complications that may well indicate alcoholism. She is on a status level closer to many employees and so can directly discuss and counsel more easily. Also, because her duties are less exacting that the physician's she has an opportunity to develop special knowledge about alcoholism. She can especially become familiar with treatment facilities outside the company.

Not to be overlooked are employee counselors who have professional backgrounds in clinical psychology and psychiatric social work. Such persons can serve as specialists in alcoholism, counseling and referring to outside sources for specialized medical care, or, in conjunction with an industrial physician, can make up a treatment team. Some companies have relied on a psychologist and an industrial nurse for their treatment. Still others have relied completely on their employee counselor, who decides how much purely medical support he needs. Such a counselor can explore the possibility of vocational rehabilitation, often having had training in estimating the extent to which job demands are matched to employee abilities. A closer matching of these two factors can contribute substantially to recovery from alcoholism.

Despite the many possiblities within companies for treatment, outside possibilities probably play a more prominent role. Many of the current treatment techniques are not easily used within a company medical set-up (i.e., group therapy). Furthermore, it becomes a problem to schedule and follow through on the long-term routine called for in many therapies. These can best be carried out in a clinic or hospital away from the company.

Communities vary widely in the kind and amount of treatment resources available. Some will contain none at all and a company will have to rely on its internal facilities completely. But many larger urban centers will have a variety of possibilities.

As a community resource for the rehabilitation of alcoholic employees, management will find local affiliates of the National Council on Alcoholism, founded in 1944, in 75 locations throughout the United States. The N.C.A., the only voluntary organization working for the prevention and control of alcoholism on a national basis, has helped these 75 communities to "do something" about the illness in their respective areas.

Physicians, scientists, members of the bar, law enforcement officers, health officers, social workers, and other professional people work with interested laymen to educate the public about the nature of alcoholism as a disease.

Many of these local affiliates of N.C.A. maintain alcoholism information centers and referral services for alcoholics. Business and industry have found these resources tremendously helpful in directing alcoholic employees toward the proper treatment and eventual arrest of their disease. Many companies now help support these local voluntary organizations in return for their help as an outside resource in curbing the problem of alcoholism in their own firms.

For the seriously ill alcoholic employees who may require short-term hospitalization, more and more doctors and hospitals are treating alcoholism as a distinct illness. Over 3,000 general hospitals now accept alcoholics as patients, compared with fewer than 100 about ten years ago. Any local medical association will have available knowledge in this respect. Many county and state medical associations have established subcommittees on alcoholism and many of these groups have brought pressure on local hospitals to offer specialized treatment for alcoholic patients.

When companies consider the inception of a company program on alcoholism, there is often wonder if such a move places too heavy a load on the company's medical department or might necessitate enlarging the medical staff. Yvelin Gardner, Deputy Director of the National Council on Alcoholism says: "We have found that an alcoholism program in a company does not mean adding to the medical staff. It really reduces its load. Less time is spent in the aggregate on alcoholics with such a program than when there is none at all."

Company management will find during the operation of a program to combat alcoholism among employees that a relatively small percentage of alcoholism cases brought to light and placed in the company procedure for treatment will need immediate hospitalization. Management will also find in many areas that any outside treatment facilities which might be needed in various instances (whether in-patient or out-patient) within the particular community are facilities which are connected with a medical school and a research center. Thus treatment fees are less. In other instances the fees are very modest, and in still others only nominal. Types of treatment vary widely, but can usually be secured on an out-patient basis. Thus the typical treatment available fits smoothly into a company program. Schedules are often available at different times of the day, allowing an employee to receive treatment without too much job interference.

Probably the most widespread and readily available resource outside the company is Alcoholics Anonymous. In a sense it is not "outside" at all, because AA members probably work for the company. But many of the traditions of AA prevent them from "breaking their anonymity" and so the company may be unaware of their presence. On the other hand, one of their Twelve Steps to Recovery calls for them to carry their program to persons who still suffer. Consequently, treatment personnel in a company can contact the local AA group, letting it be known that they are eager to use AA members in therapy, and on a confidential basis. Many AA's are not too sensitive about their anonymity but do not want to take the initiative in breaking it. So they often welcome such an opportunity. But they still want as much protection as possible and desire to do their "Twelfth Step" work in their own manner.

In many companies, treatment personnel have developed closer, longstanding relationships with AA members in their own plant. Often the recoveries from the efforts of these people are as numerous as from other techniques. Usually other treatment efforts have accompanied exposure to AA, but membership in a group has provided a follow-up influence that is unavailable in other techniques. In a substantial number of instances, the company keeps specific lists of AA members, working on a highly confidential basis for compatible matching of AA sponsor and newcomer.

Still other companies strongly encourage AA groups within the company, providing meeting space and policy approval. Some programs rely almost exclusively on such AA groups; an AA counselor is hired by the company and regularly contacts new cases as well as helping the company-lodged group with its older members.

AA can, of course, be used as a community referral without any "inside" aspects at all. It is quite easy to become acquainted with a group by merely attending open meetings, learning who its secretary is, how the group manages requests, and what its general approach is. Many an AA member has made his first contact with a group because some physician, nurse, or personnel counselor where he worked told him about such specifics as place and time of meetings and gave him a simple, accurate description of the Fellowship.

Such treatment personnel have taken cases to their first meetings, continued to check on their attendance, and explained AA to the alcoholic employee as he tried to "make the program." Certainly one of the first facilities for the company doctor or nurse to become familiar with is AA and its local characteristics. To the extent that he knows AA, he can help his case affiliate. A newcomer to AA often has many false notions about the group (for example, that it is a religious denomination) and during the crucial weeks of first contact a knowledgeable nurse or doctor in the company can clarify a great deal.

But there are limitations to AA. Probably one of its most obvious is that it is relied on too much. Harried employee counselors, doctors, and nurses have frequently made wholesale referrals to AA, assuming that thereby the matter was managed. Too frequently they have forgotten their own responsibilities. They have assumed that AA can do more than, in reality, it can. Any newcomer approaching AA, as well as those on the program for a time, continues to need medical and psychological support. Referral to AA can be thorough, followed-up, and explained, or it can be casual, short-lived, and confusing to the alcoholic. Successful affiliation depends in no small measure on a thorough, not a piecemeal, referral.

Finally, it should be observed that many alcoholics do not "take" to AA, while others seem to accept it at once. Consequently, there are numerous times when AA referral of any kind does not work. Sometimes it is a matter of time, and the employee will accept the program after repeated exposure. But there are also those who just aren't attracted. In other words, AA is a potent treatment device, but if it is relied on completely there will be no productive treatment results for a substantial number of cases.

19 Early Discovery of the Alcoholic Employee

The presence of sound policy and substantial treatment sources insure two of the necessary parts of a program. They do not, however, provide supervisors with the information needed to identify an employee early in the alcoholism process when treatment efforts are more likely to succeed. Only by focusing on these signs and clues separately can they be highlighted sufficiently to provide the base for action. Policy communication and supervisory training are natural ways to underscore them, but before this can be done the specific behaviors must be spelled out.

Actually this question introduces the hard-core problems in any industrial program on alcoholism. First, how can supervision decide whether an employee is, or is not, an alcoholic? Second, how can the supervisor himself be motivated to use a policy if he decides a drinking problem is present and thereby encounters the third and toughest problem of all—how to get the alcoholic employee himself to accept treatment referral.

What is the strategy of early case finding? Simply that it is unnecessary to reach the stage of utter defeat before treatment can be successful. At one time the belief was widely held that an alcoholic must fully hit bottom before he would respond to therapy. But we now know that this sense of "hitting bottom" can be brought on much earlier in the process, provided the illness is labeled openly and dealt with directly. The purpose of early spotting of alcoholism, then, is to "raise the bottom" so that the employee can get treatment before he has deteriorated badly and has less chance of recovery.

There are at the moment no biochemical tests or clues for early alcoholism, and the prospects for such indexes are not too bright. The behavior involved is what calls it to our attention. So the clues to the presence of alcoholism must be social ones, not chemical or pharmacological ones. And, on the job, it is the immediate boss who is in the best position to observe and interpret these signs. The broad strategy, then, is to help him perform the task.

What are the main on-the-job signs of a developing alcoholic? There are two ways to look for answers to this question. One is to get alcoholics themselves to describe certain job-behavior patterns of theirs as their illness progresses—the "inside-looking-out" view. The second way is to see the same behavior through the eyes of the boss—the "outside-looking-at" view. These boss-noticed clues are probably more valuable. Employed alcoholics go to great lengths to cover up their problem—they are the real cover-up artists, not their bosses— so it is what the boss notices rather than what the alcoholic covers up that is helpful. Of course, what is really important is to compare the inside and the outside views so that what the supervisor notices can be added to the earliest possible signs.

Alcoholics themselves describe certain clues as first appearing on the job. The hangover is the earliest. It is a combination of thirst, headache, fatigue, jitters, and nausea. Often it produces avoidance behavior—staying away from supervisor and peers. Hand tremors are noticeable results of hangovers and later become independent clues regardless of hangover.

But in the early period of the illness they are outward signs of internal hangover agony. Unfortunately, it is possible for the developing alcoholic to suffer hangover without too many outward signs. Because he wants to do everything possible to prevent his condition from coming to the attention of those who work with him, he becomes very skillful at covering up hangover.

For that matter he is the chief agent of "cover-up." His boss is not the one who performs this function. His peers do more than the boss, but he does most of it. Where the hangover is concerned, he tends to do an excellent job at it, developing a routine such as preparing his work in advance of the hangover so that he will be faced during hangover with tasks that involve "going through the motions."

Alcoholics describe, as the next earliest sign, various kinds of absenteeism. But because his chief purpose is cover-up and protection of the job from damage, absenteeism is not of the traditional, off-the-job kind. Rather it is of a partial nature during the work day, and he makes intense efforts to avoid repeated, accumulated absences of the obvious off-the-job type although these begin to appear. One of the earliest on-the-job signs is a peculiar mixture of on-the-job absenteeism with the more traditional kind. To be specific: forms of partial absenteeism that begin to appear are such behavior as leaving the job post for an unusually long period of time, being late to work, leaving the job early, and taking long lunch periods. These are intermingled with a *slightly* higher than usual amount of traditional off-the-job absences.

Again it is important to note how this early sign is, like the hangover, muted and covered up by the problem drinker. He goes to great lengths to use a kind of absenteeism that is less conspicuous and less job-threatening. Where on-the-job accidents are concerned he is even more cautious, taking great pains to avoid lost-time accidents that might bring him under-close scrutiny. So on-the-job accidents, of a minor or lost-time variety, are not early clues. Absenteeism is bad enough for him, and in the early period even that is resorted to in bits and pieces and disguised as much as possible by its partial nature.

As his illness progresses, signs appear on the job that he finds more difficult to hide. They begin to stand out like a sore thumb. They come from the fact that both physical and psychological changes occur. Even if he does not have alcohol in his bloodstream while at work, these signs are difficult for him to manage. But if he has been drinking during the work day, some of these signs become even more obvious. Increased nervousness, jitteriness, and irritability are hangover symptoms that become more intense and more difficult to hide. Hand tremors become more gross. Work pace becomes uneven —cycles of intense output followed by slumps.

At this point, work performance begins to suffer noticeably. Avoidance behavior is quickly resorted to so that a face-to-face encounter with a supervisor can be avoided. Red or bleary eyes, coupled with a flushed face, often are present, even though there is no alcohol in his bloodstream. In place of accidents, money problems begin to be reflected into the job situations. Garnishments, levies, and liens show up in personnel offices.

Now, the traditional stay-away forms of absenteeism increase and the alcoholic employee develops all manner of implausible excuses and explanations for them. He is still struggling to protect the job but with much more obvious methods. These strange, odd, and improbable explanations are more damaging than useful, but he still goes on trying, despite the fact that now his illness is beyond effective cover-up and is coming out in the open regardless of what he does.

Not only does he resort to lying about absences, but he begins to lie about work operations and details. The lies pile up and contradict one another because he forgets some of them or gets them mixed up and gradually begins to believe the whole conglomeration himself. Unlike the usual liar, who knows full well he is lying, the alcoholic comes to believe his lies and fabrications. As a part of this dishonesty there arises a special indignation and sensitivity to opinions about his drinking when expressed at work. In many instances this expresses itself as paranoia: he is more suspicious of fellow workers and in private ruminations more intolerant and resentful of them.

Now the alcoholic employee becomes more and more aware that he is unable to cover up. He is forced to seek more drastic ways to reduce the visibility of his symptoms. Quite early in his illness he experiments with morning drinking as a way to avoid absences and hangovers, with their increasing withdrawal pains of tremors, jitteriness, and nervousness. This works on an intermittent basis and helps muzzle many of the signs he is trying to hold in private. But it also creates new cover-up problems. Once started on work-day drinking, there arises an irresistible urge to continue. So early morning drinking before work leads to drinking at lunch time, and this, in turn, to devising some way to drink on the job. This produces additional clear-cut clues.

Under these conditions, certain physical and psychological signs are accentuated. Red or bleary eyes become more obvious. There is a mixture of alcohol aroma and "breath purifiers." Lunch periods become longer, but, probably more important, there is often a sharp, noticeable mood or personality change after noontime drinking. If he had been morose and subdued he becomes affable and gay. Loud talking is apt to be in sharp contrast to his earlier behavior that day.

At this point, one of the sharp signs of definite alcoholism occurs. Alcoholics behave consistently different when intoxicated than do normal persons when intoxicated. This personality change—Dr. Jekyll-Mr. Hyde—becomes an obvious danger sign.

Throughout this entire process, work performance has steadily declined. The cyclical "spurts" help prop it up, but it suffers noticeably. Both quality and quantity suffer, but quantity probably suffers first because of the extra caution needed to avoid accidents and the energy used to manage hangovers. Unfortunately, this general decline does not appear as one of the earliest signs because the employee is protecting the job in any way he can and job-performance rating is one of the most sensitive spots. But poor performance begins to alternate with capable performance, and this appears early enough to justify management concern about alcoholism.

In contrast to this inside view—from the horse's mouth, so to speak—what do bosses of alcoholic employees tend to see as early signs of a developing illness—the "outside view"? The alcoholic's boss, rubbing shoulders with him in a daily routine, should have the best opportunity to observe early signs. In addition, the boss administers a whole series of formal restraints and techniques for controlling employees—time clocks, inspectors, rules, and disciplined work routines. These operate to spotlight deviant behavior and so make it easier to notice clues of early-stage alcoholism.

But despite these aids to observing early clues, the alcoholic employee still does a good job of covering up his earliest symptoms. Bosses tend not to be aware of hangover signs until they become relatively gross, and not too much even then. One reason for this is that they tend to see, among their employees, a goodly number of hangovers. They themselves have probably experienced such symptoms on intermittent occasions and so are less sensitive to the possible inplications. There is a reluctance to intrude themselves into the private life of an employee. In addition, there is a casual good humor about hangovers if they are admitted or observed. It's something that must be "sweated out" but is of no unusual consequence.

Of course, much about the hangover in the early period of alcoholism lends it to cover-up by the sufferer. The discomfort is internal and, with an effort, can be covered over by a facade of "a cold" or "didn't sleep well" or "sinuses are acting up." There are no easily seen, uniform, outward expressions of the condition. As it gets more frequent and more pronounced, the withdrawal symptoms will become severe, but in its early form —hangover—it is easily "lost in the shuffle" as the supervisor goes about his many daily tasks involving numerous employees, one of whom is the developing alcoholic.

In many ways the same can be said for the disguised forms of absenteeism that make up other very early signs. The boss becomes annoyed by these, especially disappearance from work place, but they are not linked with a drinking problem very easily and so the boss is merely inconvenienced mildly rather than alerted to an illness. His first inkling probably begins when real off-the-job absences force him to seek replacements or shuffle his work assignments. But the developing alcoholic is acutely aware of this—one of his chief techniques for denying that there is anything wrong with his drinking is to claim his job is unaffected. Probably the chief clues that begin to be noticeable to his immediate boss are the forms of "partial" absenteeism, especially unauthorized departure from his work post for a substantial period.

In summary, there are numerous reasons why the earliest signs of alcoholism on the job go virtually unnoticed by the person most likely to see them. Alcoholics themselves, looking from the inside out may be acutely aware, but they do such a good job of cover-up that their bosses do not notice. *One of the chief problems of early identification lies in making supervisors more conscious of these earliest signs—hangover symptoms and traditional absenteeism intermingled with partial absenteeism.* Certainly developing alcoholics are not going to disclose these clues, so only the awareness by their immediate boss can be of any practical use.

On the other hand, it cannot be concluded that bosses of alcoholic employees do not soon become aware of the problem. They do. As the disorder progresses, the problem-drinking employee becomes less and less skillful at cover-up. As this occurs it is difficult for a reasonably alert boss not to observe the signs. Work routines bring them repeatedly to his attention. Repeatedly he discovers he has to watch him more closely than other subordinates. This grows from partial absenteeism on the job. But other signs are beginning to appear to join this one. Being production-conscious, the boss begins to notice the mixed nature of performance—both good and poor within a given block of time.

Interestingly enough, the paranoid suspicions, resentments, and sensitivity of the employee about opinions and questions concerning his drinking are not noticed too much. Apparently these are mainly a part of private delusions, easily disguised to an authority figure.

Presently, the boss becomes aware of the kind of absenteeism that is a real problem—the traditional, off-the-job kind. He must make replacements more often and listen to more ridiculous explanations; often he has to stretch his work force to cover the alcoholic's job because that guilt-ridden employee had not reported he was going to be absent and there was no time to get a replacement. The less even, more spasmodic work pace becomes an obvious threat to the production of his alcoholic subordinate. Less and less can the boss rely on him. More and more he does not know what to expect.

But the boss becomes acutely aware of him when the alcoholic turns to daytime drinking as a way to handle his problems. For a while the morning drink before work reduces the signs, but not for long. Soon the boss becomes aware of the fact that, in one way or another, his employee is drinking during the work day. This is a reflection into the job of loss of control —once morning drinking starts there is a strong likelihood it will trigger continued drinking during the day.

So the boss begins to be painfully aware of the smell of alcohol or breath purifier. The alcoholic employee becomes very "tricky" at avoiding him. The boss may be too busy to notice the before-work morning drink—after all it does temporarily and partially manage things. But he may note the sharp personality change after lunch-time drinking, which often brings with it loud talking and generally relaxed, uninhibited behavior.

In other words, the boss may miss the more subtle, very early signs, but he certainly does not miss those somewhat later signs that tend to happen the most. In a very basic sense, it is almost impossible for him to be unaware of them. Probably the crux of the whole thing is lower quantity and quality of work. This really hurts. A supervisor is judged by how well he can get his men to perform. When one of them becomes a poor producer he is painfully aware of it and of the probable reason why.

To help him in this regard he also has the grape-vine. Despite its many inaccuracies, it probably carries one element of truth: alcohol is a big part of the problem. In many ways, fellow workers often know about a drinking problem before the boss. They may have observed his off-the-job drinking, his tendency to keep on after everyone else had quit. What it all adds up to is simple: the boss is aware of the problem and what its general nature is, although this awareness develops as the illness moves towards its middle phases.

There are, however, some specific situations that alter this general conclusion. Occasionally a supervisor will be in charge of mobile, relatively isolated jobs. These jobs are free from close supervision and detailed work routines. Since many of the early signs of alcoholism must be seen at close range with a high degree of exposure, such jobs can easily nurture developing alcoholics with practically no clues developing until the late-middle and even late periods of the disorder. Also, there are job situations that call for both employees and supervisors to move about from shift to shift. So as a boss becomes aware of a drinking problem in one of his men he can merely brush it aside—"I can put up with him until a new foreman takes over."

Furthermore, at certain levels of American society—lower status situations—there is substantially more tolerance for these various clues. In a sense they are expected, even looked upon as somewhat normal. Under such circumstances it is difficult for a supervisor to notice "clues" for an illness when such behavior is an accepted way of living. In addition, executive alcoholics enjoy a great deal of freedom from supervision and scrutiny and so they are much more difficult to identify early. They tend to be very careful about absenteeism, avoid drinking in any unusual fashion with persons from the job, and so frequently become full-blown alcoholics with very few on the job knowing it.

Even though the immediate boss usually becomes painfully aware of a drinking problem, it is also possible for medical personnel to develop early case-finding information. Numerous companies require a medical department visit after three to five days of absenteeism. This often provides the physician an opportunity to be on the alert for signs. Since there is no clear, physiological base for diagnosing early alcoholism, this cannot be a hard and fast matter.

There are, however, certain diagnostic signs that may be clues to developing alcoholism. There is very good reason to believe that real minor illnesses increase sharply with the alcoholism process. These seem to center in upper respiratory ailments, pharyngitis, bronchitis, and gastro-intestinal upsets such as acute gastritis, colitis, diarrhea, and duodenal ulcer. Obviously, other than alcoholics suffer from these. But there is reason for at least suspicion when these illnesses occur repeatedly. Even if a physician is not available, such clues can come to the attention of an industrial nurse. She or the doctor is in a position to help a supervisor come to a tentative conclusion about whether or not a drinking problem is present. On the other hand, there are ethical problems of confidence in disclosing medical information. Certainly, however, such medical personnel can help sow the seed in the mind of the alcoholic himself.

Probably the biggest problem in early identification, however, is not to reaffirm what the boss probably well knows. On the contrary, it is to get him to realize its significance. As already noted, he tends to be largely unaware of the earliest signs on the job. Even at this point there has probably been a sizeable amount of damage done to home and social life. By the time the boss clearly sees the problem, the illness has, in all probability, disrupted many parts of the employee's life outside the job. What it boils down to is: although the boss comes to see many of the signs of alcoholism, he does not link them with a developing illness that is already well on its way toward becoming chronic. So the problem is to inform the boss about what these signs mean. Except for the earliest signs, job circumstances will make him aware of many of the clues, certainly enough. What he does not realize, however, is what serious consequences these signs indicate. If the supervisor's awareness of the earliest signs were increased and his realization of the significance of those clues he tends to see sharpened, early identification would be much more effective.

One final difficulty plagues early identification. How can heavy drinking on a steady basis be distinguished from early alcoholism? In all probability, recurrent job disruption has not yet occurred, so that particular index is not available. The only distinguishing feature at this very early period appears to be the hangover. Many heavy drinkers do not experience what is commonly known as the hangover. Their drinking is heavier, but inconspicuous.

On the other hand, the developing alcoholic clearly experiences hangover as one of his earliest on-the-job problems. Apparently the hangover is sharp and clear. The early-stage alcoholic must contend with it, anticipate it, and devise ways to pretend it is not there. Actually, it is the early version of severe withdrawal symptoms that will become almost beyond endurance later. Certainly it is true that the heavy drinker may occasionally experience intense hangover just as the normal, social drinker will if he drinks a great deal. But these are probably much less frequent, less regular than the developing alcholic's.

20 Reaction of Supervisors to Alcoholics

If you are the boss of an alcoholic employee it is one thing to recognize on-the-job signs of the disease but quite another to use an alcoholism policy if one is available. In other words, a good policy may be in effect, but its fate lies largely in whether or not the immediate boss will use it once he is aware of early signs and their significance. The question is simple but basic: how can supervision be induced to use the alcoholism policy as soon as possible after they realize a drinking problem is present?

Only one other question is more difficult—that of how to get the problem-drinking employee himself to accept treatment. Actually, the two problems are so intertwined that they form the hard-core problem in practically any company program on alcoholism.

Although the reaction of supervisors to alcoholics varies widely—one boss may be a middle management boss with fairly high status to whom a general foreman alcoholic reports, while another may be a newly appointed foreman just up from the ranks who finds he has a semi-skilled operator alcoholic on his hands—there is still a good deal of common experience for numerous bosses of alcoholics. By examining this common experience, clues for getting supervisors to use the alcoholism policy should appear.

What is it like to be the boss of a developing alcoholic? Above all, it is painful; it is agonizing. Unlike being the boss of a neurotic employee, or even a psychotic one, there is a painful seesawing back and forth—to handle the situation oneself or to report it. This is not deliberate, willful concealment. It is rather an annoying mixture of emotions, a dilemma; and, impelled to act both ways at the same time, the boss vacillates; he is undecided. There are definite pressures playing on him to use the alcoholism program, but there are others, almost equal in strength, pressing him not to use the policy. While this tug of war goes on within the boss the alcoholic employee gets worse—keeping in mind that even the most alert supervisor probably missed the earliest signs and became aware of a drinking problem after substantial deterioration in other parts of the alcoholic's life.

What are these conflicting pressures to which the boss is subjected? First, there are the positive ones, those pushing him toward use of the policy. Probably the most motivating influences here are those centering in poor job performance. It is the supervisor's job to get a "whole man for a whole day" regardless of what type of job this may be. Most of the time this does not happen with the alcoholic employee. So the boss must watch over, supervise, check up on, and plan more closely, the entire work of this employee. This adds to his worries and takes time away from other supervisory tasks.

Moreover, there is the increasing problem of absenteeism. First, it is frustrating to put up with partial kinds of absenteeism. But it is even more upsetting to many work routines when the boss has to find replacements on the spur of the moment for traditional off-the-job absenteeism. This frustration increases if the supervisor must arrange overtime for replacements. All this can be still more irksome in those companies—and they are numerous—where there are strong drives under way to reduce absenteeism.

But it is lack of predictability for the alcoholic employee that adds fuel to the fire. The boss never knows what to expect from him. The boss can't count on him, compared with his other subordinates. At the same time, the boss will be unexpectedly pleased by a stretch of good work or an effective series of tasks well done. So he becomes uncertain of this employee, never knowing when, or under what circumstances, the alcoholic will "act up" or be all right.

All this makes the boss uneasy. He becomes apprehensive because the problem-drinking employee may well put him in a bad light. The boss is troubled by anticipating that some incident such as a customer complaint, a foul-up with another supervisor, or an embarrassing incident may happen. Then he will be asked why he had not done something sooner about this employee. Furthermore, this can reflect up and down the lines of authority. It is also interesting to note the role of possible accidents. Although supervisors of alcoholics often describe the alcoholic worker as relatively free of on-the-job accidents, they are nonetheless concerned about him and fear what might happen, even though it rarely does.

The immediate boss is further aggravated by the bad effect the alcoholic employee has on other employees working around him. Often his work piles up on other employees. They resent the fact that this particular employee is not holding up his end of the job. Then, too, they become disgusted with the need to be more concerned, anxious, and helpful for this one person. After a time it begins to look like favoritism. The boss, too, is sensitive to the problem of playing favorites, so he is just that much more ready to resort to the alcoholism policy.

The readiness is increased by a frequent feeling that the

alcoholic employee is putting something over on him. At first, the boss did some mild cover-up. Also, it is only natural in our society to try to help—especially if you are a supervisor. So as the boss tries to help, tries to reason, tries to figure out what is wrong, he begins to get the impression the alcoholic employee is taking advantage of him. Slowly the boss comes to see his relationships with his alcoholic employee as a one-way street. In short, this particular employee expects help, understanding, and cover-up, but gives very little in return.

But all positive pressures are not purely job oriented. Most supervisors are concerned about family welfare. So bosses of alcoholics tend to consider using the policy because they believe it would in the long run help out both the employee and his family if something constructive were tried. There is typically a fear that family disruption will endanger job performance. But there is also a strong value attached to family life. Since there has probably already been deterioration of family life, and echoes of this have reached the boss, his concern that something be done has mounted.

Finally, his readiness is often encouraged by the support of his immediate boss. In many ways, there are usually at least two levels of supervision directly involved, sometimes three. Often these key people in the boss's life become fed up sooner than the immediate boss and will fully support action by the boss to use the policy. On the other hand, they tend to leave the final decision to their subordinate. But their support provides a background against which the boss can feel that the case will not blow up in his face if he decides to use the policy.

From this description it would seem the immediate boss would not hesitate to use the alcoholism policy. But, unfortunately, he does. And often with very good reason. Probably the foremost of these reasons is the desire of the boss himself to help the developing alcoholic overcome his drinking problem. Rather than turn him over to the impersonal treatment of a company policy, he often chooses to try to handle the matter himself. He reasons that it is the duty of a good supervisor to take an interest in his workers' problems, hopes, and despairs. So, often the boss tries to understand and handle the problem himself. To do otherwise would be an admission of failure as a supervisor. But to be successful in efforts to help his problem-drinking subordinate would be very satisfying to the boss. In addition, it would salvage a good man for the company.

Then, too, the boss tends to believe that to use the policy is a matter of last resort, after everything else has failed. Like many others he usually has the stereotype of a late-stage skid-row bum in mind. So the employee must be showing symptoms consistent with this late-stage image before he is eligible for the alcoholism policy and its program. If and when the fellow gets that bad, figures the boss, he should be turned over to the medical department or whatever part of the company the policy calls for.

In the meantime, the boss figures: "I will do all I can to help him, *not* label him." In other words, the supervisor tends to believe that resorting to the alcoholism procedure is "finish," that if there is still a possible chance the employee should be shielded from a label akin to a skid-row "lush." But if he gets *that* bad, then, and only then, should he be turned over to the medical department.

So, the boss is apt to spend an undue amount of his time trying to reason, cajole, and listen to his charge. He is apt to go out of his way to show him extra consideration and to help him. Often the foreman holds a strong value of "standing on your own two feet." As a result he sees this employee as a child to be helped to independence rather than to be treated by "outsiders." In addition he may well have been successful in such efforts with other employee problems unconnected with alcoholism and naturally tries the same approach here.

In essence, this is a supervisor fulfilling the general role of boss. He is willfully and deliberately trying to meet the expectations of such a role. One of the chief notions of the human relations school of supervision is to understand and help employees work out personal problems that hurt job performance. In doing so he is not deliberately protecting the alcoholic so he will not come to the attention of some other authorities in the organization.

But he—the boss—is managing the matter himself. The end result is that the boss does not use the alcoholism policy, except as a last resort, if at all. By this time the progression of the disease has probably taken the employee well into symptoms that respond very slowly to any kind of treatment.

A variety of other considerations buttress this reluctance to make use of the alcoholism policy. Often its use is regarded as equal to discharge. Once on the alcoholism procedure, reasons the boss, there is a good chance the employee may be separated from the company. There is, of course, a rough truth in this. Because of hesitation by the boss, the disease has progressed to a point where discharge or some form of separation is a likely outcome. The supervisor notes this coincidence and reasons that it might have been better not to have used the program at all since it resulted not in rehabilitation, but in discharge or separation—so a vicious circle develops.

These reactions are reinforced by the likelihood that the boss often regarded the alcoholic as a capable, able worker. Certainly there were times when he did not so look upon him. But in many ways the boss is apt to remember work performance when it was not directly affected and also to note periods when the problem drinker would snap out of it. It is this latter factor that especially creates a hesitancy to use a policy. After trying very hard to help this employee overcome the problem, it is easy to become overly hopeful when periods of "snapping out if it" occur, and frequently they do. The alcoholic employee is shrewd enough to see trouble coming; he is worried enough to try to control his drinking.

So he does frequently straighten out, only to relapse. But at the time of temporary improvement the boss is apt to see it as a sign of hope and so continue his efforts to treat the case himself rather than "turn him in."

A cluster of secondary factors back up these main reasons for the boss of an alcoholic not using the policy available to him. The family of the employee may be one. The boss is reluctant to hurt the wife and children, for example, by what he believes to be a stigmatic label. Again there is the late-stage, skid-row stereotype operating in this reluctance. To the boss it may be an illness, but it is also a moral stigma, and to label the employee alcoholic is to apply that stigma and so hurt his wife and children.

Closely akin to this reason for hesitation are work situations where the boss and the alcoholic had worked with each other for years as peers, had known each other off the job intimately, and had often drunk together. Such a situation can be aggravated by fellow workers seeing their work associate as a well-liked, popular person even though he does drink too much and cause them some inconveniences. These points are sharply accentuated if the boss is a first-level supervisor. In such a spot he is the man in the middle, trying to identify with both management and his men. In such an in-between status he is particularly sensitive to friendship and family reasons.

Finally, there are instances in which certain organizational factors will create hesitation. Supervisors may foresee an uncomfortable and time-consuming mix-up with the union, and, unless a policy is well-launched, this can be a reality causing many bosses to hesitate. In addition, challenges by the union can be embarrassing because the boss may not have the formal records to back up his use of the program. There is also the need to fill out records and forms in a world already full of paper work. It is also quite possible for the boss to feel unsure of himself when the medical department comes into the picture. He may feel uncertain about backing there because, as he sees it, he is not a medical man and so cannot diagnose an illness condition.

What all this amounts to is really quite simple. There is a readiness among supervisors of alcoholics to use a policy. But this readiness is stymied by perplexities that leave the boss floundering and puzzled, vacillating between using and not using. The problem is to free him from this confusion and indecision. In a very real way he is looking for help out of his dilemma.

One basic way to help him is to relieve him of the feeling that it is his task to manage the problem alone until it becomes intolerable. This is not an easy communications problem. Both in policy communication and in training, however, it is possible to show him that a policy and its treatment possibilities can work with him, sharing the "headache" and the treatment effort.

Certainly, he is still a part of the treatment picture—it is he who must primarily execute, if necessary, the discharge policy, if realistic treatment efforts fail. But he need not go it alone; he can get company help in his desire to restore the employee to health.

Above all he should *not* be given the feeling that someone else has taken over; rather, he has resources within the company he can call on for help. It is at this point that the term "sick" is crucial. The boss can get medical and specialized aid for an illness in one of his employees. Since he will freely admit he is not a medical man, there is a reasonable basis for him to accept help, realizing that his relationship with his employee during treatment is also a most important part of the therapy.

It is helpful to point out that supervisors of alcoholic employees have usually regretted offering the helping hand too much and too long. Typically, they agree it did more harm than good to try to manage the matter all alone. As they look back on the experience they see how the problem drinker was manipulating them by playing on their sympathies, by being contrite and humble when lectured, and by "snapping out of it" for a time.

Two other points should be made over and over. First, the supervisor has nothing to be ashamed of because he does not understand the problem. His indecision and vacillation are quite understandable. No aspersions are cast on him because in the midst of a busy work world he is not knowledgeable. Above all, do not accuse him of deliberate, calculated concealment, which implies he has clearly decided what to do, when actually he has been largely seesawing back and forth. In short, tailor all training and communications about alcoholism to the probability that he has been torn both ways, rather than assume he has deliberately joined with the alcoholic employee in a determined effort to prevent his probelm from coming to light.

In other words, it is quite easy for personnel men, industrial physicians, and management officials to develop a false picture of how the supervisor reacts to an alcoholic employee; namely, the boss is a culprit who identifies immediately with the problem-drinking employee and blocks therapy because he covers up. At this point, these persons are engaging in just the kind of stereotyping that permits the immediate boss to see only late-stage, skid-row symptoms as indicating alcoholism— the content of their stereotype is different, but the process is the same.

Second, continually state the simple point that the skid-row, late-stage, "lost-weekend" picture of an alcoholic is as false as it could possibly be. Just as those working with the boss may see the boss falsely, so does he falsely visualize what an alcoholic is like. This false notion is so ingrained in American thinking that it cannot be attributed solely to the supervisor by any means. It is largely due to our obsession with skid-row bums and late-stage symptoms. But it is not beyond alteration. By continuous, simple emphasis, both direct and indirect, this mental image can be shifted. Only when the supervisor works from an early and middle-period image, rather than a late one, can we hope for adequate referral to a policy.

21 Acceptance of Treatment by the Alcoholic Employee

Even if supervisors, in order to come to resolve their see-sawing quickly in favor of using the policy, do think in early-period terms rather than late-stage terms and do relax their "go it alone" attitude, there still remains the question: how to motivate the alcoholic employee himself? This is the toughest of the hard-core problems. A big start is made on it if the immediate boss behaves decisively, using early signs and sharing his problem with a treatment facility of some kind. But there still remains the question of how the employee himself might be motivated to accept both the nature of his problem and the treatment offered.

This, of course, is the chief purpose of the entire program. Everything is designed to set the stage for getting the alcoholic to accept available therapy. In a very real way, the entire effort is directed at motivating the alcoholic employee, leaving the treatment to specialized facilities. Obviously, all incentive for the alcoholic to accept the program cannot come from the job, but it can play a major part. In view of the fact that sobriety will mean a drastic, almost total change in his style of life, that it will temporarily cause him unbelievable pain, the potential incentive present in the job must be added if at all possible.

Up to the time the boss decided to refer him to the company program, what had been the chief reasons for his abnormal use of alcohol? Apparently the job situation must help reverse these motives and introduce him to satifying new ones. He has *learned* that alcohol can help him satisfy some of his most basic needs. It does more than just relax his anxieties. It often provides him with recognition and emotional response from drinking associates, making him feel confident, worthy, sought after, loved. In addition, it may well provide him with a chance for new experiences by helping him revolt against undesirable restrictions; he can shed adult responsibilities of work and family. By repeatedly experiencing a reduction in these basic drives in drinking experiences and situations, he learns an alcohol response to them.

Whenever he feels tensions due to these unsatisfied drives he seeks immediate relief from them by the use of alcohol. It is quite probable that he has unusually high needs of some type, i.e., security or response. So he learns the value of alcohol in reducing them more intensively than drinkers with more normal needs. The rewards he gets thereby more than make up for weak and confused social punishments and threats. Actually, he has probably met with few clearly-defined, fore-warned, automatic sanctions in areas of his life where he is deeply involved.

If he is married there has probably been confusion and vacillation on the part of the spouse even greater than that of the boss. He has often forestalled such action by giving up drinking for a time if the spouse shows real signs of separation—a family version of "snapping out if it." Very few direct sanctions have come from friends, relatives, private physician, or neighborhood.

But there have been increasing signs of rejection. Friends, reluctant to directly interfere, have shunned him more. Nasty episodes with the spouse increase. Children are showing they are embarrassed and know something is wrong. His doctor may well have warned him. He himself can see he drinks differently. Probably he withdraws from friends more than they reject him. He finds recognition and response in drinking groups and temporary drinking companions. Usually he holds values of self-control and feels very guilty because these have been violated by his use of alcohol. In sum, he know something is wrong, but he has learned to get satisfaction for basic needs by the use of alcohol and in the drinking situation.

So he does not want to give up alcohol, but he is deeply disturbed by his deviation and the trouble it is causing. Early in the problem he begins to recognize something different about his own drinking. He is worried about the consequences of it. He is in the classic spot of wanting to eat his cake and have it, too.

The way out is simple: be secretive, hide the differences. Use surreptitious methods to drink. These will reduce the barbs from friends and family. They will also provide a base for denying to himself that anything is wrong.

But soon he finds he must drink more, a good deal more, to get the same satisfactions he had received somewhat earlier. In other words, he gets drunker than before and his disguise becomes less effective. His surreptitious drinking becomes more obvious and ineffective for his purposes.

So to prove to himself that there still is nothing wrong he develops a whole network of excuses, explanations, rationalizations, and clever lies to justify his use of alcohol. These also serve as defenses against the outside world; they are beginning to see through the camouflage and behind the secretiveness.

As he moves into the middle period of alcoholism he is developing a private world of excuses, lies, justifications. These delusions are shared, if at all, with drinking associates. In this way a sense of uniqueness, of not being understood, of being "in here" while "they" are "out there," develops. A part of this delusion system is an effort to relieve the mounting self-hate. So fantasies of accomplishment are added, near-impossible projects planned, and imposing gestures made.

These look odd and even ridiculous to those around him. So he withdraws more, isolates himself more. But he cannot down the feeling that he has lost his will power. His values of self-control continue to haunt him and provide the base for self-hate. As he uses alcohol more and more this self-hate becomes stronger and stronger. There is a bitter disappointment with himself, an impotent rage directed inward.

The "alcoholic thinking" serves one main purpose—to prove to him that there is nothing really wrong. Such assurance allows him to hold onto his learned source of satisfaction, alcohol. But there are definite defects in this, defects such as a sense of will-power loss and self-hate. *This, however, is managed more and more by protecting the job from damage.*

Despite many irrefutable signs that there is something very much wrong with his drinking, he can point to the unaffected job and claim this shows he is still in control: thus the care to avoid absenteeism and accidents, the intense concealment on the job. Not only does he share the emotional and economic investments in the job with millions of workers, but he has another reason to be deeply involved: the job is his most convincing proof, both to himself and to those who are criticizing him, that he is in control.

The Achilles' heel in all of this alcoholic thinking is the job and the self-control it signifies. Should this bulwark crumble, he will truly have no way to manage his self-hate. Obviously, he would have lost his self-control and might well feel relieved if someone helped him to find new ways to meet his needs. In other words, it is obvious he will not usually bring himself to accept the alcoholism program. But should he no longer be able to point to the job for defense, his sense of self-hate will become intolerable, and he will feel relieved that a way out is given him.

How can the alcoholism policy and the boss help at this point? The attachment to alcohol as a way to reduce the tension of the unsatisfied needs for recognition, response, security, and new experience is deeply imbedded. The immediate reduction of these needs by alcohol and the drinking situation has so far proven far stronger than social sanctions. Under these circumstances what is needed is as strong and clear a series of undesirable consequences—social sanctions—as possible, from as many sources as possible.

In short, a *crisis* is needed. Until the suffering alcoholism causes him is greater than the rewards it gives him there is little chance of treatment success. He must lose something important to him, or at least face the very real possibility of losing it, before the link between alcohol and need satisfaction can be weakened and, hopefully, broken.

Certainly this crisis, or crises, would not immediately replace alcohol as a way to secure tension reduction. They would, however, help to shatter the learned attachment to alcohol, providing an opportunity for other ways of reducing tension to develop. What is needed first is some way to knife through the network of rationalizations and private delusions so that the attachment to alcohol as a tension reducer can be directly confronted.

The one tool available at this point is job threat, made simultaneously with an offer of treatment opportunity. If this "constructive coercion" is without loopholes, is communicated "loud and clear" by a decisive supervisor who is backed by the union shop steward, and is tied directly to poor job performance, it has a definte chance of shattering the old pattern, of "raising the bottom." It is striking hard at a highly sensitive area with the full force of both management and the union. It is coupled with a *heavy positive* emphasis on rehabilitation, on a way back to normal work life. If this latter is effective, even partially, it will act to teach new ways to reduce tensions and thus produce substitute satisfactions. In short, the entire strategy centers in demonstrating to him that the job is no longer unaffected, and doing this with such clarity and finality that it will set in motion a self-hate which will be relieved by the opportunity for rehabilitation.

This scheme is by no means without defects. At certain levels of our society the self-hate is not as clear a part of the emotional reaction. For example, in what is broadly referred to as the lowest strata there is far less awareness of abnormal behavior. Employees from these backgrounds will not, in all probability, respond too well. The same can be said for some personality types. Obviously there are those whose security needs are so unusual that enforced cooperation of the kind embedded in the policy will be intolerable—it is quite possible they would be damaged even further. Another very obvious difficulty lies in the need to move swiftly and decisively both in applying the policy and its sanctions when realistic progress is not made.

Despite these deficiencies, the strategy has much to commend it. Probably its chief asset is that it presents the developing alcoholic with a firm positive definition of his condition coupled with an offer of help. But this is joined by a predictable consequence—job loss—in such a way that the employee cannot manipulate his way around the consequences of his drinking.

The immediate boss has a definite role in the effort to get the alcoholic to accept the nature of his problem. His first contribution is to make sure the alcoholic employee does not manipulate him into further indecision. The employee is very able at playing on his boss's indecision to what he believes to be his advantage. The immediate boss has to resolve his "seesaw" to put the employee on the program; *he has to keep on being decisive after the policy is activated.* The alcoholic has a tremendous need to have his own way. He makes powerful attempts to control others' thoughts and actions, especially those in authority.

The ingratiating tactics of the alcoholic can beguile the boss away from the strategy. He will be docile and contrite and snap out of it in a very attention-getting way. These are strategems to relax the boss. He will encourage the "let's go it alone" tendency of the boss by criticizing therapy and casting aspersions on it. He is struggling to keep the problem in the man-boss relationship, believing he can handle it here, but fearing that if he goes to the treatment facility he will truly have to admit he has lost control. It boils down to merely this: the boss must remain firm, pointing out that he will administer the policy based on the prognosis of the treatment facility, but will back him completely while he is undergoing treatment.

The boss will often be reluctant to approach the matter directly, but he can add considerable weight if, *from the very beginning,* he firmly, without hesitancy, tells the employee what the problem is and what the company is going to do about it. *Little lasting change is possible until the problem is in the open and can be dealt with directly.* He can legitimately take the position that he has a right to do just this because of poor job performance. As a matter of fact, on this latter point he can provide some recognition by pointing out how job performance may have improved after treatment.

Of course, there is the danger of being too hard—overemphasizing the job threat and playing down the positive offer of help. There is also the problem of being too soft, being for example, overawed by the seniority of an employee. Their seniority makes them "untouchables." Either one of these attitudes will weaken the strategy. There is also the problem of too close supervision—"breathing down back of the neck." If at all possible this must be avoided. The boss must accept the reasonable prognosis of specialists and realize that slips do happen in rehabilitation and must be absorbed up to a point.

The boss can add a great deal if he can physically accompany the employee to the first contact with the program, i.e., to the personnel "middle-man" or to the medical department. If both he and shop steward can go it is even more effective as a ritual, and if he can accompany him briefly on one or two subsequent occasions it will add to the impression of interest and conviction. In addition, the boss will have a greater impact if he hits him with the explanation during a period of remorse, such as when he is "coming off of one."

Through all of this the boss can underscore that the employee is suffering from an illness; his malady is acceptable as such. The company proves this by giving him treatment help, not disciplinary punishment. The supervisor can thus bolster the idea that the employee is not unique or unusual, pointing out that others have attained sobriety. If he has a "success" case who is known to the employee he can use this as a model. Also, he can point out that there has been a great deal of treatment success throughout the country. There have been failures, too, but the prospects are good for his getting better. In short, the company is providing a chance to re-enter the normal work role; it puts the emphasis on positive opportunity but still insists it will discharge if this action becomes necessary.

Athough it may be somewhat difficult to work out, coordination of this strategy with the spouse's reaction can be explored. She, or he, as the case may be, may find that the firm, direct, open, and active position of the boss and the company will clarify her reactions. She has probably been condoning, covering up, and providing ego support for some time, despite her awareness of the problem. But she becomes more and more disgusted.

If her exasperation can be coordinated with the reaction of the boss, backed by the company and the union, the key non-alcoholics in the employee's life will have provided a series of social sanctions capable of competing with the immediate satisfactions of alcohol. Truly, a crisis will be precipitated, and the stage set for therapy. But the shock must be a true one, just as the job threat must be forthcoming if tested. She must not only threaten to leave him but give distinct signs of abandoning him to his own fate, without her support.

On the other hand, this approach must be viewed with some caution. The wife is probably more vulnerable to manipulation and thus may waver, allowing the alcoholic to play her off against the boss, a maneuver at which he is a past master. Her own personality may strongly need the domination and "mothering" possible when her husband is drinking. For that matter, the mother, instead of the wife, may be the family figure. Here the possibilities of faltering in a firm shock policy are probably even greater. But the boss, or personnel representative, may well explore a combined shock, if their judgment indicates a reasonable firmness in the spouse.

It should also be kept in mind that this kind of negative motivation has a point of diminishing returns. In other words the "bottom" has a bottom. Constructive coercion strategy can clearly be carried too far.

Favorable response by the problem-drinking employee to the program may also be aided by varying certain job conditions. The question of job transfer always appears as a possibility. A certain amount of job content change may be helpful, but it is doubtful if out and out transfer will contribute very much. Above all it seems desirable to maintain the same supervisory relationship after therapy has started.

On the other hand, job changes that remove the employee from the emotional supports of friendly fellow workers may be helpful. It is definitely helpful to reduce the amount of freedom to move around completely on his own. In other words, removal of obvious drinking opportunities during the work day can help some to sustain the impulse to remain sober. If it is possible to assign him to work with a stable, able, relatively sober "partner," it can be a positive influence. Reversed, it can cause real damage. Of course, many jobs do not lend themselves to this arrangement and cannot be created just for rehabilitation of one employee.

It is always possible to reassess his abilities and try to use them more fully. Vocational rehabilitation of a thorough kind could help him positively. If the personnel department is equipped to make such appraisals it definitely might be of help. Various employment offices, both public and private, might be used if deemed advisable.

A final point should be made regarding the *positive* side of this motivation scheme. The entire strategy assumes that the therapy available will offer to the alcoholic employee a realistic hope that sooner or later a life of sobriety will be more rewarding than "crises" of alcoholism. This places a heavy burden on treatment referral sources. But only the acceptance of such a task will make therapy realistic. Certainly, the work place will have done its job full well if it delivers to the treatment facility, whatever it may be, an employee who has been constructively coerced to seek help and whose readiness to change has been started in the desired direction.

22 The Company Program

It takes time to develop the ingredients of an alcoholism program. Each of the parts calls for changes. Although these do not usually require any new personnel or budget increases, they do require changes in attitude, knowledge, and procedure of current personnel. Because traditional notions about alcoholism have developed sterotypes that do not alter easily, these necessary changes take more time than in changes where fewer emotionally-charged ideas are present. For example, some companies have found that it takes much longer to develop and write a policy on alcoholism than it does to write new employment policies. Others report that only after a dozen or so years of a policy do the majority of supervisors "unfreeze" their attitudes and freely use the policy without hesitation.

But probably the slowest part of a program lies in treatment. Often a company has to stimulate interest among hospitals, psychiatrists, and private physicians. Following this, the treatment know-how must develop. But this also takes time, since treatment techniques are just now emerging and so are largely unevaluated. In addition to this time-consuming aspect, there is the problem of influencing the alcoholic himself. As we have seen, he will initially deny, resist, try to manipulate. It takes more time to get him to treatment than it does the victim of more traditional illnesses.

Time is also consumed in working out the bugs of a policy, especially when a union is present. Even though there may be initial union acceptance and assurances of cooperation, there is time consumed in actual scrutiny of a specific case who is a union member. It takes time to establish a new definition in many minds, to explain the purpose of a policy and how it works, to allow for, at least, a degree of informal resistance and dragging of feet.

In much the same way, supervisors do not quickly shift their thinking away from long-held ideas. Training about early clues requires repetition at intervals to effectively combat late-period images of alcoholics. It takes time to demonstrate that using the policy does not inevitably mean discharge or separation. Successes pile up slowly and are not noticed for at least a year or so. The supervisor has to be assured numerous times that he is not expected to handle such employees but is expected to get help in supervising them. In other words, it takes time for supervisors to learn the value of a staff service and make use of it.

Unfortunately, however, there is frequently a desire for quick results. When these are not forthcoming, or resistances are strong, or one part of the program works and another does not, there is a tendency to lag or drop. Practically speaking, these are what would be expected. Results will come by consistently and firmly pressing the different parts of a program steadily over a period of time. Gradually they will become a part of on-going routine. With time, weak parts can be strengthened, failures studied, and purposes widely explained.

Company programs on alcoholism have been largely confined to large companies with good-sized staffs. Their success and example have greatly speeded up the acceptance of alcoholism as a treatable illness. On the other hand, it has also fostered a false notion that only big companies have the facilities and staff to start and maintain a program. In fact, however, smaller companies can easily make and use a policy, with practically no expense. In some ways they can do it more easily and economically than a big one. Probably more important, the alcoholic employee is by no means limited to large companies—he is as apt to be in small ones as in big ones.

Since the employed population of America works in small, medium-sized, as well as large companies—nearly one out of every two persons employed in the U.S. is owner, manager, or worker in a small businses—alcoholic employees are probably represented somewhat evenly in all size companies. It may be, however, that these employees are a bit over-represented in small ones. Many small companies do not have the staff to screen and select employees as carefully as larger ones. They cannot recruit as widely and so are forced to hire "left-overs" more often. The alcoholic worker, especially in lower-status occupations, is likely to be well represented among such recruits. Furthermore, contrary to popular belief, the number of small businesses in the U.S. has increased slightly per 1,000 population in the last ten years. For these reasons it seems probable that the alcoholic employee is present in at least equal, if not greater, numbers in small companies as in large.

But his impact on the small company may well be greater than on the large corporation. The cost of his poor work cannot be afforded as easily in a small company. In the large company, mediocre work is not felt as keenly or as quickly and is balanced out more easily. Because of more intimate, personalized work relations in the small company, his problem is apt to be more visible. He causes adverse effects on morale of fellow workers more quickly.

In addition, the entire hiring and replacement problem tends to be more difficult in a smaller company, so it may be slower to consider replacement of an alcoholic employee. For that matter, an alcoholic spouse of an employee can have quite an impact on the work situation, especially in a small company. The worry, frustration, and perplexity of an alcoholic wife or husband can reduce work efficiency, increase absenteeism, and create personality problems.

Furthermore, the small company seems to be more tolerant —infinitely more so—than in larger industry. It is more personalized; management comes to know the employee more as an individual and to concern itself more with his personal problems. So they are reluctant to discharge unless there is a very flagrant reason. Thus the alcoholic employee often remains, costing the small employer in poor performance. Added to this is the smaller employer's frequent dislike for going into the job market—so he tends to keep the alcoholic employee, if he is not *too* bad, once he has hired him.

In short, the small company has as much reason as the big one to consider the alcoholic employee a personnel problem. It is, like the large one, often reluctant to admit it has any alcoholic employees. But once it realizes that it probably does have them, the small company can easily put together the parts of a program and achieve as much success with it as a large firm. And, regardless of size, the parts of a program are the same —policy, early identification, treatment resources, motivation of immediate supervisor and alcoholic employee, plus time.

But certain features of small companies make it necessary to tailor the general strategy of a program. Usually, small businesses have fewer supervisory personnel; there are fewer "levels" between employee and manager or owner. Often there are no staff personnel at all or only part-time ones. Thus a small manufacturing company may have an office manager who, in addition to his regular duties, does *all* personnel functions.

Or it may be that a small company is closely tied to a parent organization, but geographically is widely separated from both the parent and other small units. Under such conditions the unit is in many ways autonomous, but it still can draw on the resources of the larger organization. In contrast, the small company may be largely without direct or indirect connection with any larger firm and, as such, stands almost completely on its own two feet. Frequently, such businesses organize loose trade associations that help meet common problems.

There are many different kinds of small businesses. They vary by the extent of supervisory levels between workers and owner-managers, by the number of personnel staff available, by the possible tightness or looseness of control by a parent company, by the strength of trade associations to which they might belong. Their diversity seems to be noticeably greater than among large companies.

Furthermore, small businesses are more apt to be in smaller towns and cities, away from large urban centers. There is some tendency, however, for a mild concentration in suburban areas. This, however, does not provide the multitude of possible services and information of the urban center.

In sum, the small company probably does not have internal facilities such as full-time medical and industrial-relations personnel. Some may have ties with a parent company that provides a degree of help, but not on an immediate basis. The industrial nurse is probably the most frequent employee who could work into a program. In addition, there is often a half-time personnel man who could easily become aware of and administer a program.

Another difference lies in the less formal organization of small companies. A family atmosphere is more prevalent, and there is less emphasis on formal authority as such. The personalities of the men who own and manage a small firm often give it an individual quality. Their leadership and guidance determine policy and its effectiveness. Sanctions such as job discharge after therapy for alcoholism are thus more individualized, more informal.

Smallness also sharply limits the number of alcoholic cases a firm may have. In a company of 300 employees it is reasonable to believe that five or six employees are probably alcoholic, assuming a normal age and sex ratio. This is not enough for sustained awareness. There is apt to be an off-again, on-again pattern of experience with alcoholic employees. There will probably be times when none at all are present. Furthermore, these will tend to be lumped with other problem employees such as the emotionally immature and physically deteriorated. Rather than think in terms of a specific problem employee, the small employer is more likely to think of problem employees in general and how to handle them.

Because of these differences from big companies, the general strategy of a company alcoholism program needs to be fitted to small business. All the basic ingredients of a company program must be used, but altered somewhat for a smaller firm. Thus policy must have the same basics—recognition as an illness, provision of treatment help, and job loss "if reasonable progress is not forthcoming"—but these can be individualized. It need not be a highly formal statement but can be recognized policy among management. It is easier to write. There are fewer segments to object and delay a policy decision. Many small companies can quickly and easily form, communicate, and carry out such a policy without too much concern over communication coordination, or lip service. Management is close to all phases of an operation and can immediately see that a policy is carried out—for example, in thousands of small companies, management and ownership are in the hands of the same person.

But there is apt to be more reluctance to use the constructive coercion, or job discharge, aspects of a policy. Because of the more personalized nature of policy, fewer medical personnel to set clear prognosis, and the greater tolerance of smaller companies, this vital part of a policy may easily be watered down. It may even be forgotten entirely if a union is present. So where policy is concerned, the small company must be more concerned with follow-through, setting the possible point of discharge as realistically and fairly as possible.

The infinite tolerance of small companies can seriously weaken a policy. This is as much a matter of top management attitude as supervisor's attitude. To a sharp degree, the greatest problem a small company faces in putting a policy into use is the tendency of the manager-owner to give the alcoholic employee infinite numbers of last chances. *In other words, small companies are more prone to be over-lenient on the job threat part of a policy, especially their top management.*

Where treatment outlet is concerned, the small company will probably have to tailor its program more drastically than larger companies. In practically all instances it will have to depend on outside facilities. If it is located in an urban or suburban area its problem is quite different from the small company in a relatively rural area. A part-time personnel man can easily learn about information centers, specialized clinics and hospitals, and specialized physicians. AA groups are readily available and can always be found regardless of region. Even if a small company does not have a personnel man at all, nor an industrial nurse, its supervision can easily find out about treatment facilities, often available on a free basis.

Such a company usually has a physician for some type of medical consultation; he can be asked to become aware of facilities. Personal physicians of management can be asked to learn about treatment possibilities. If an industrial nurse is present she can readily be assigned the task. In short, such a company, located where some type of treatment is in all likelihood available, need only alert itself in some fashion.

But the isolated small company has a greater problem. It must rely almost completely on its physician and AA. To a marked degree it can urge its physician to learn about alcoholism, to discover its various treatments. For example, the *Manual on Alcoholism,* prepared by the Committee on Alcoholism of the American Medical Association, is readily available from the American Medical Association. In addition, this committee can provide additional literature directed toward the private physician. But in close conjunction with this possibility there is AA. This fellowship is present in many smaller towns and even hamlets. A smaller company can find and employ on a *necessary* job a member of AA who can act as a direct contact with that fellowship.

AA members often make excellent employees. It is not difficult to contact a group. Usually they are listed in the local phone book under "Alcoholics Anonymous" and an interested outsider can learn more by asking when he can attend an open meeting. It is also possible that a current employee is already a member of AA. By letting a group know of his interest, an employer can probably hire an AA member, but he should do so primarily because he can do a necessary job, not because he is an AA.

Furthermore, most outlying towns and small villages are today relatively close to a large urban center. Rarely is it more than a four or five-hour trip to a population center where more specialized treatment is available. Again, it requires very little time or energy for a particular supervisor, a nurse, or a private physician who works with a small company to learn about facilities in nearby cities.

Possibly the only inside resourse for many small companies is the industrial nurse. Often she has conflicting feelings about an alcoholic and a company policy must be carefully explained. But she possesses a professional background that enables her to learn quickly, once she is given the opportunity and the encouragement. She is a valuable adjunct to any kind of therapy, as well as to AA. She is especially valuable in early identification and referral.

In a small company she comes to know many aspects of a particular health problem. Since alcoholism has numerous medical complications, she often can help sow the seed of awareness in an alcoholic's thinking. She can be especially useful in learning about treatment facilities in the area and keeping informed on what they are, how to contact them, and what they cost.

For those small units of a large, widely-scattered company there are possibilities of calling on the company's medical department. There is even the possibility of stimulating a company-wide policy by the adoption of an "individualized" approach in the unit. Help can be requested of all company medical and personnel staff as a treatment outlet, whether or not a company-wide policy is in effect.

But geographical separation and lack of knowledge of the specific situation will make such outlet information somewhat abstract. There is very little substitute for on-the-scene knowledge and action. Home offices can give general information and background help, but management of local units must usually find specific treatment outlets. And for those small companies who have only very loose relationships with a parent company—a car dealer for a large automobile manufacturer, for example—there is probably very little help from the parent company.

This, however, does not preclude the possibility of a company with many outlets throughout the country helping its dealers in health matters. As a matter of fact, it would be one of the most effective ways to reach thousands of small businesses. Mere suggestions about how a policy might be formed, what a program's main points were, would be of great value. The basic conclusion is that the diversity of types of small businesses does not permit any standard pattern. Rather it indicates that the immediate management can easily learn about treatment facilities in its own situation and be prepared to use them, whatever they are.

This raises the question of how company policy in an organization of many small, separated units could be most effectively organized. It seems reasonable for "headquarters" to set up the policy basics, communicate them clearly and often, but leave to the local unit the problem of treatment outlet, early identification, and training of supervision.

Finally, the private physician has certain features that the small company might well consider. There is a substantial minority among them who are interested, often knowledgeable, and willing to follow through with a case. This is certainly not the majority, but there are signs such physicians are increasing. Although these interested physicians do not have proven treatment techniques at their disposal, they do not reject the alcoholic patient as a moral degenerate. Identification of some such private physicians by an interested management of a small company, and their general use and encouragement, would provide both a treatment outlet and the expansion of knowledge within a key professional group.

Then, too, there are private physicians scattered throughout the country who specialize in the treatment of alcoholism. Usually there is such a doctor within a 200-mile radius of any business. Knowing who he is and how he can be reached can often provide the basic treatment for a small business.

The small company has one consolation in its search for available treatment. Almost any type of therapy will help some and will often help a great deal. Thus, if no clinic or specialized treatment is available, an interested private physician will be useful. If a specialized physician is not easily available, AA exposure may have a substantial effect. *The big point is: try something.* There is, *at least,* a fifty-fifty chance.

Where early on-the-job signs of alcoholism are concerned, the small company enjoys an advantage. The intimate, personalized, family atmosphere enables a closer knowledge and awareness of early signs such as hangover, symptoms and partial absenteeism. Informal contacts combine with work routines to increase the general visibility of early signs. The man-boss relationship has many personal aspects, many of which bring confirming clues from neighborhood, family, work associates.

But the biggest problem in small companies is to produce an awareness of the seriousness of these early identification signs. Various features of small businesses often provide a better opportunity for early identification, but there is probably less connection between these clues and the significance of them. In early-identification discussions with supervision, greater emphasis needs to be placed on the danger these signs indicate than on the signs themselves. In many ways, supervisors in small companies know about a drinking problem quite early but do not realize the danger. The big need is for supervisory training to bring to their attention what these signs mean. In addition a small company may have only a few cases over a period of time. This will also tend to reduce the significance of early signs. *In short, early-identification training must be strongly linked with probable alcoholic developments later in the illness for results to be effective, especially in smaller companies.*

Despite this problem, possibilities of early identification are still enhanced in small companies. More supervisory persons are apt to see and contact the developing alcoholic than encounter him in big companies. Supervisors shift around less; employees are transferred less, although they may fill multipurpose jobs. If they do, they are seen frequently by numerous supervisors as well as by their main one.

It will be harder for the developing alcoholic to cover up. Partial absenteeism of all kinds will usually be far more visible. Results of drinking during the work day cannot be hidden as easily from supervisors because there are fewer employees in physical quarters that are relatively small. Personality changes after noon-time drinking may be lost in a mass of employees, but stand out clearly among relatively few employees.

All of this makes it easier for an alcoholism program in a small company to motivate the immediate boss to use the program. If the significance of early signs are clear to him he has a good chance to think in terms of early-stage signs rather than late-stage characteristics. This reduces one of the basic obstacles the boss has in referring an employee to a program: thinking in skid-row terms—i.e., "if he *finally* gets that bad I will do something about it." Since early signs tend to be more visible in the small company, the boss in a small company has an excellent chance to refer an alcoholic employee to a program very early in the disease, *provided the significance of those early signs are appreciated.*

Also, the tendency of the boss to engage in do-it-yourself therapy with the alcoholic employee will tend to be less in small companies. Certainly this characteristic of the supervisory role will be present. But many of the reasons for reporting a problem drinker to a program will be stronger in a small company and so overcome this tendency of the boss to handle the matter himself. Thus he can more easily be put in a bad light by the alcoholic. The boss more frequently comes into contact with, and under the scrutiny of, the owner-manager. Incidents involving the alcoholic employee can quickly embarrass the boss. Bad effects on fellow workers can readily be seen by the boss. Poor work performance shows and cannot be covered easily. His absenteeism, both partial and off-the-job, are easily noticed. The boss in a small company, in short, becomes more sensitive all along the line. This sensitivity to the alcoholic employee causes him to be more motivated to use the policy.

In some respects the alcoholic himself can be more easily influenced in a small company. It is much easier for him to be told in very simple terms, "Your work is unsatisfactory, and we believe you have a drinking problem." There are few levels of management, and all of them can say the same thing to him at one meeting. Many small companies are not unionized so the alcoholic cannot play management against the union. There are practically no go-betweens, such as personnel men or counselors, between him and the treatment offered. He does not have many persons whom he can manipulate between himself and facing up to admitting his problem and accepting therapy. Thus the full impact of the job threat can be brought home to him.

The small company can, compared with the large one, truly precipitate a crisis. It also probably has a better chance to coordinate its policy with the reaction of the spouse because of personalized relationships both off and on the job. In no other place in the work world does an employer have a better chance to *bring a drinking problem clearly into the open and deal with it directly*. And there can be no more basic principle in therapy than this one. The weak point, however, remains the tolerance of manager-owners of small businesses. All the advantages of the small company may easily be lost because management will not resort to discharge after reasonable therapy. If the alcoholic employee discovers this to be the case the opportunity to motivate him will be lost.

This tolerance of small companies toward the alcoholic employee also hampers their need to let a program mature, let it operate for a number of years. If discharge of an alcoholic employee is not forthcoming after reasonable efforts, then time will not help the program to grow, but rather will hinder it. Furthermore, the fact that small companies often have periods when they do not have an alcoholic employee or are unaware of any, makes them less likely to work the bugs out of a program through using it steadily. Consequently, small companies have a problem with the last necessary part of an alcoholism program—sustaining it over enough time so that it will be used, understood, and supported.

Two simple ways of overcoming this problem are open. First, small companies can develop a program through their trade associations. Second, they can develop a policy for problem employees in general, with the approach to alcoholism as a part of it. Both of these possibilities are characteristic of many types of small business and so are practical.

Thus a trade association with many affiliated small businesses often helps out its members by personnel administration techniques and employee health hints. Such trade groups could easily summarize and circulate the experiences of small companies which operate alcoholism programs. This could be done anonymously, although there is a sharp tendency today for companies with programs to allow the use of their name.

There are, of course, groups of small employers which operate a joint health program of both treatment and training for supervision. Such a group could include alcoholism easily enough, since it is a prominent health problem. Among the cooperating companies a common policy could be worked out and a program of training and treatment operated through the association for each member company. In this way there would be a substantial number of cases and a program could be used enough to get it into working order.

Probably more practical, but less effective, is a broad policy on problem employees, with alcoholism and its program a prominent type of problem. Rare indeed will be the small company which does not have employees who fail to produce as they were expected to do. They may do so because of lack of ability or skill for the job. They may be misplaced. They may just naturally have friction with their boss or he may be inadequate as a supervisor. They may not have grown up emotionally or may be physically ill with such widespread maladies as heart disease or cancer. Alcoholics probably rank just after these types of employees in numbers, so there is every reason to include them among "problem employees."

Since practically every company will experience some employees who fall in the "problem" category, it has every reason to systematically plan what it intends to do about them. For example, what simple but effective program can it have for the misplaced or the physically ill? A simple policy on misplacement can be worked out. It can state merely that to avoid misplacement there is a need to know job tasks and the details of those tasks so that the company can match job and employee more easily. Such a policy might call for a replacement effort of a reasonable type for a misplaced employee, just as a policy on alcoholics would call for a reasonable degree of help and treatment aid. Both might then call for discharge if these efforts proved futile.

Even more relevant would be a policy on physical illnesses. The alcoholism program would most resemble this type of employee problem, especially in at least providing treatment information, if not support. It differs in its sharp emphasis on discharge if progress does not develop. But otherwise, alcoholism is a health problem just like heart disease. The small company can include it among its employee problems, using the alcoholism program whenever it is necessary and reporting on it regularly as a part of the company's over-all approach to problem cases.

A simple conclusion emerges from all of these points. Small companies have definite reasons to form a program on alcoholism. They also have many opportunities unique to a smaller concern. They can easily, and without expense, form a policy and launch it without extensive consideration and delay. Early identification is simpler with them. Both the immediate boss and his alcoholic employee can typically be motivated more easily than in a large company. Because of these advantages, and because of the spread of the alcoholic population through all types and sizes of industry, great strides in reducing alcoholism can be made if smaller businesses will develop their own policies and programs.

23 Summary

1. Formulate a company policy which explicitly recognizes alcoholism as an illness. State clearly that those employees affected are given the same benefits of medical attention, insurance, and general personnel practices as persons with other health problems. In other words, make alcoholism a "respectable" disease with which no guilt feelings should be associated.

2. The cornerstone of a successful company program is solid and unanimous support by management. Such affirmation breeds confidence from the top down and makes all personnel gradually aware of the sincerity and practicability of such a move.

Once the program is announced by management, allow the progress of its execution to be slow and easy and without fanfare. In other words, "easy does it," for it takes time for the essential objective and its worth to circulate down through the ranks of a company. Include alcoholism in the description and management of health problems in company bulletins and other publications, stressing particularly that alcoholism is a *respectable* disease, comparable to tuberculosis, heart disease, or cancer.

3. However, at the time of inception of a new company policy toward alcoholism among employees, hold special supervisory meetings outlining this new step of management. Inform supervision about the "warning signs," early detection, attempts of "cover up" by alcoholics, also the futility of "cover up" by supervision in order to protect his employees afflicted. Explain the progressive nature of alcoholism. Make supervision directly responsible for referral action.

4. Include shop stewards, or other union officials, in early plans for steps 1 and 2. Avoid any intimation of "crusading." Aim the new policy as the relief of a difficult problem for supervisors and foremen as well as for the treatment of alcoholic employees.

5. Supervisors and foremen are the key personnel who determine the success or failure of an alcoholism program. Supervision must motivate the alcoholic employee toward treatment. They must be thoroughly sold on the program and then allowed to try it out in their own way. Management should let supervision know that it is realized there are reasons pulling them both ways—for and against referring alcoholics for treatment.

The company must establish a straightforward policy and provide a simple basis for resolving the superintendent's or foreman's indecision. Management must let it be known that it does not believe the boss will willfully engage in "cover up" and especially point out that the supervisor *is not losing an employee, he is retaining one after suitable treatment.*

Due to the progression of alcoholism, the supervisor is actually doing the employee a personal disservice in not motivating him toward treatment.

6. After referral for treatment, the medical department (or in the cases of smaller companies, outside medical consultation, community clinic, etc.) works closely with supervision, labor relations, safety, insurance, employment, and other

departments which might be involved. Insofar as possible maintain the confidence of the afflicted in the personnel records. The medical records are, of course, inaccessible.

7. Admittedly, one of the greatest difficulties in handling alcoholics is to get them to acknowledge in the early stages that they *do* have a problem. The medical department, personnel manager, employee counselor, or whoever handles the alcoholism program, should "sell" the alcoholic employee on the program—by a mixture of precipitating a crisis with a job termination or an offer of a way back through treatment support *backed by management all the way down the line.* Remove the alcoholic employee's last defense by clearly, but simply, telling him fairly early in his illness what his problem is and how it will result in job loss if continued. But underscore the positive part of treatment help.

8. Utilize the resources of all community agencies. These include general hospitals, community committees and information centers on alcoholism, Alcoholics Anonymous, private physicians, and the clergy. If such resources are few, help, with other companies, to create such resources.

9. Post-treatment rehabilitation of the alcoholic employee involves, first of all, a medical evaluation to determine fitness for return to work. Follow-up counseling is then undertaken whenever possible to consolidate gains made through treatment and to provide encouragement and support for the employee in the hope that the disease can be kept in an arrested condition permanently.

Index